CW00819979

Marrow Bones

Marrow Bones

English Folk Songs
from the Hammond and Gardiner Manuscripts

Selected and Edited by
Frank Purslow

Revised with New Notes and Commentaries by
Malcolm Douglas and Steve Gardham

Foreword by
Vic Gammon

efdss
englishfolkdance&songsociety

The English Folk Dance & Song Society
2007

The English Folk Dance & Song Society
Cecil Sharp House, 2 Regent's Park Road
London NW1 7AY, United Kingdom
www.efdss.org

Produced for the English Folk Dance & Song Society
by Nigel Lynn Publishing & Marketing Ltd
106 High Street, Milton under Wychwood, Chipping Norton
Oxfordshire OX7 6ET, United Kingdom
enquiries@nigellynnpublishing.com

British Library Cataloguing in Publication Data
Data available

Library of Congress Cataloguing in Publication Data
Data available

ISBN   978 0 85418 202 0

1 3 5 7 9 10 8 6 4 2

Typeset in Plantin by
Nigel Lynn Publishing & Marketing Ltd

Music setting by Julian Elloway

Printed in the United Kingdom by
The Alden Group Limited, Witney

CONTENTS

PREFACE

WHEN *Marrow Bones* was originally published, if I had been told that over forty years later, it would be re-issued in a format I had only dreamed about, I would have been completely disbelieving. I admit the original edition looks 'cheap and nasty' today, but in those days conditions were very different. By the late 1950s it had become obvious that the folk song revival had taken off, and there were thousands of young people, with very little cash, armed with guitars and a desire to sing – but with nothing to sing! Ewan MacColl and Bert Lloyd, following the example of Pete Seeger and Alan Lomax in the US, had shown the way, and the EFDSS decided to follow – reluctantly in some quarters! As it happened, *The Penguin Book of English Folk Songs* got there first, but I became rather proud that I could mention several singers, who later became well-known, whose original fund of songs relied heavily on the contents of *Marrow Bones*. At that time, apart from a few scholars, I was almost the only person who had any knowledge of the contents of the manuscript collections in the Vaughan Williams Memorial Library; moreover I had become acquainted with the vast collections of broadside and ballad-sheets in the British Museum (as it then was) and the Bodleian Library here in Oxford. This had led me to the conclusion that English folk song had relied for a large part of its dissemination on this despised 'street literature' – a view considered heretical by a good many members of the Society. So I set to work and, believe me, I now envy the modern folk song enthusiast with their computers and the internet. You have no idea how lucky you are!

Frank Purslow
Weald, Bampton, April 2007

FOREWORD

AS a teenager hungry to explore English traditional song there was something of a scarcity of material to consider. The *Penguin Book of English Folk Songs* was a classic text in the formation of the outlook of many people interested in the subject. I and I know many others, were suspicious of the published works of Sharp and his contemporaries as we knew from the work of Reeves and others that those songs were bowdlerized and prettified. Yet, outside spending time in the Vaughan Williams Memorial Library, it was hard to access stimulating and what we considered authentic material.

Then *Marrow Bones* came along. Not all the problems of the original book were the fault of its editor, who I understand felt that his project had been untimely ripped from him before it was mature. The book was presented in small print that was really hard to read, had the most twee drawings you could imagine, and with its so-called perfect binding, fell apart with the minimum of regular use. The notes were incomplete and fragmentary. All this said and speaking personally, I have to rank *Marrow Bones* as one of the ten or so most significant books I have ever owned.

What struck me most about the collection was the quality of the songs and in particular the tunes. One of my first ventures into folk journalism was to write a review of the work. Thankfully, I cannot find it to quote my juvenile self but I remember praising the quality of some of the songs. When, knowing I had to write this piece, I asked the singer Chris Coe what she thought of *Marrow Bones*, she commented on the great songs and the great tunes and how the collection had provided a foundation for revivalists interested in English song. Great tunes are there in plenty; a few of my favourites would include 'Swansea Town', 'Fair Susan I left', 'Charming Molly'. The book provided key material for many revivalists with such songs as 'The Shoemaker's Kiss', 'The Tailor's Breeches' and 'I Live Not Where I Love'. Looking through my disintegrating copy I am surprised how many songs I still sing, or perhaps how many songs I sing which originated from or have been influenced by, versions in *Marrow Bones*.

The book reflects the aesthetics of the folk song movement (both the earlier and later branches) and is replete with versions of many canonic songs. Yet in a small way it also shifted perceptions and understanding. In *Marrow Bones* you will find some downright oddities, pieces that Sharp and his contemporaries would never have published. Sometimes this is for the obvious reasons of prudery – there are plenty of songs dealing with sexuality in its comic and tragic aspects. But there are other pieces that point to the breadth of the vernacular singing repertory in the early twentieth century and before, such as the wonderfully insulting 'Compliments Returned', the paean of praise to bachelorhood 'Serious Tom', the rarely encountered 'Sour Grapes', the oddly intertextual 'An S-O-N-G'. These and others pointed to a song repertory wider than the aesthetics of 'folk song' had led us to believe existed.

It is good to see *Marrow Bones* in print again with serious improvements in presentation and editing. It is a monument to the work of Gardiner and the Hammond brothers, those heroic Edwardian oddballs whose efforts, along with those of the other collectors of the period, saved material that otherwise would have been lost. I have the feeling it will go on sustaining the revival of the performance of traditional song among generations who were not born when the book first appeared.

Vic Gammon
Newcastle University, March 2007

INTRODUCTION
TO THE NEW EDITION

WHEN *Marrow Bones* first appeared in 1965, the folk song revival that had begun in the 1950s was expanding rapidly, and a whole new generation was becoming aware, not only of traditional music in general, but of the fact that England, quite as much as the USA, Scotland or Ireland, had a rich heritage of its own. The problem for singers was where to find it. Since the publication of the seminal *Penguin Book of English Folk Songs* in 1959, the extensive song collections held at the Vaughan Williams Memorial Library had remained a largely untapped resource, though James Reeves' *The Everlasting Circle* (1960) had given some idea of the breadth of material to be found in the unpublished manuscripts of Gardiner, the Hammond Brothers, and Baring-Gould. This was a purely textual study, however; what was needed was an accessible selection of songs with their music, and that was where *Marrow Bones* came in. It didn't please every critic, some of whom would far have preferred a scholarly, critical edition of the collections; but it was very influential on the folk club movement, which seized upon the songs in it. Many of them became standards and remain so to this day. Three more volumes from the Hammond and Gardiner MSS followed and Frank Purslow's books are fondly remembered and still sought after, though they have been out of print for a long while.

It is EFDSS's remit not only to make new material from its collections available, but also to reissue out-of-print resources for which there is a demand, and it is that task which we have undertaken here. A full critical edition of the collections, on the lines of Aberdeen University's eight-volume *Greig-Duncan Folk Song Collection* or the *James Madison Carpenter Collection* (currently in preparation), must remain a dream while funding for the folk arts in England is so meagre. Meanwhile, we can at least place the songs in *Marrow Bones* before a new generation of singers. A larger format and the omission of the original illustrations enables us to present texts and tunes in a far more easily readable fashion. The second volume, *The Wanton Seed*, will follow in a year's time.

The Texts

'No-one', wrote Frank Purslow in the original edition, 'wants to sing a bit of a song that doesn't make sense, and so, as some of the collected versions were in a bad state textually, it has occasionally been necessary to supply missing lines, or even whole verses, from elsewhere. Where possible I have done this from other versions of the same song in the manuscript collection; failing this, I have had to add the missing portions from traditional versions known to me, from versions in other collections or, as a last resort, from printed broadsheets of the early nineteenth century. In the latter case, I have sometimes rewritten the broadsheet text to correspond in style, grammar or rhythm to the tune.'

This was standard practice for editors preparing traditional songs for 'popular' as opposed to scholarly publication, and is still in evidence today; though now it is usual to be quite specific about all intervention, whether it involves the introduction of material from other sources or the purely editorial amendment of texts or tunes. It was not our remit to 'restore' the original MS readings (anyone who has examined the MSS in detail will know that in many cases this would have required printing several pages of fragmentary texts for a single song) but rather to provide, so far as is possible at a remove of forty-odd years and given constraints of space, the information that someone preparing a book along similar lines today might be expected to include. In some instances, identifying the source of introduced material has been quite straightforward; in others more problematic (though reference to Alfred Williams' collection, to the repertoires of singers like Harry Cox and

George 'Pop' Maynard, with both of whom Frank was acquainted and from both of whom he recorded songs, and to broadside texts, has often borne fruit) and in others, utterly baffling. Frank himself has been generous with his time in retrieving and transcribing for us such notes as he still has; and in recalling what he can, after a very long time, of the circumstances in which he prepared the book. Unfortunately, his original working notes and transcriptions are lost; all the material was passed to Peter Kennedy when *Marrow Bones* was being prepared for print, and that was the last he saw of it. It may have perished in the fire at Chappell's premises some while later.

We have included in our notes as much detail on editorial intervention as is practicable, but relatively minor matters have generally had to go unmentioned. Frank himself says: 'It should be borne in mind that I made numerous amendments to texts ... to get rid of "redundant" syllables (to avoid too many alternatives in the musical text), to restore misplaced rhymes, and other suchlike grammatical oddities. The book was not a contribution to the *Folk [Music] Journal*, but a book to try to encourage "Folk Song Clubbers" to sing English Songs. The "Folk Cellar" had been the "Skiffle Cellar" and Tommy Steele was still performing just round the corner, when I started work on *Marrow Bones*.'

Some of those amendments would not be thought necessary – or desirable – today; to name one example, the term 'so soon as' was replaced throughout by the more modern 'as soon as'. The aspiring young folk singer of the mid 1960s was perhaps not so sophisticated as his or her equivalent in the present day, though, and may have needed more help with unfamiliar forms. Where possible, we have indicated original readings in our notes. Punctuation and capitalisation in the song texts were rather inconsistent in the original edition, so we have taken the opportunity of simplifying these, using the guidelines formulated by David Atkinson for transcribers working on the Carpenter Collection. Typographic errors have been silently corrected, but occasionally we have made larger changes which require explanation.

'The Unfortunate Tailor' is a particularly notable case. The original edition was laid out by John Brune and Peter Kennedy in the traditional way, gluing cut-up galley prints to page masters. Partway through pasting up this particular song, somebody opened a window; with predictable results. They retrieved the scattered pieces of paper, but re-assembled them in the wrong order. Frank didn't find out until the book was printed. We have restored the text to its proper sequence, and corrected an apparent mis-transcription in one line; further details are in the notes.

The Tunes

In the main, the tunes are unchanged from the original edition, though they have been completely re-set in a larger format and their layouts regularised. In a few cases, where this seemed useful and layout considerations permitted, additional small variations have been added from the original MS notation. These are indicated in the notes. In some instances, however, comparison of the MS and *Marrow Bones* notation revealed that, in a few tunes, the pitch of one or two notes had been changed. Now, it is normal to split or combine notes in order to accommodate the text set to them (singers, of course, do exactly that) and sometimes to transpose melodies to a more convenient key; but on the whole, altering the melodic structure of a tune is not done. In most of these cases we have been unable to establish whether or not the alterations were deliberate or inadvertent, or if they occurred during transcription or typesetting. They all make musical sense, and some might be considered, aesthetically, to be improvements; nevertheless, they are not what the collectors noted from the singers. Since, however, we cannot be sure whether they were accidental or deliberate, we have retained them, marked with asterisks, and added the original note pitches from the MSS. Readers can decide for themselves which they prefer to use. A few errors of typography and musical grammar have been corrected. In a few further cases, whole tunes were expanded in order to accommodate longer texts; again, we give details. In one instance, 'The Lowlands of Holland', we have added a second, rather different, set of notation made by Vaughan Williams from the same singer; our reasons for this are explained in the notes.

Accompaniment

The original *Marrow Bones* included simple guitar chords for each song, set by Frank Purslow with advice from the guitarist John Pearse. The accompaniment of English folk song (essentially an unaccompanied tradition) has always been a matter for debate, but folk song books of the 1960s and '70s almost invariably included guitar chords, just as those of the early twentieth century usually included piano arrangements. Tastes change, however, and styles quickly go out of fashion; regardless of their merits, the original settings would sound decidedly quaint to today's ear, accustomed to the very different guitar styles that have evolved in the meantime. After some consideration, then, we decided to omit the chord indications. For the reader who is a relative newcomer to the genre, we would suggest that you learn the song on its own to begin with, so that if you decide that it needs accompaniment you will already be familiar enough with it to set in a way that will allow it, so to speak, to breathe freely.

The Notes to the Songs

For the original edition, Frank Purslow's intention had been to prepare detailed background notes to the songs. While these were still only at an early, rough draft stage, he was informed that the publishers had decided against the idea, and so abandoned them; however, they were with the completed manuscript when it was forwarded to Peter Kennedy, who was liaising between EFDSS and Chappell. To Frank's chagrin, when *Marrow Bones* appeared, they had been included after all. In our discussions with him prior to preparing the book for reissue, he made it clear that these rudimentary notes should not be reprinted, so we have prepared new ones. We describe our approach in the preamble to the notes themselves.

Biographies: the Collectors

Both *Marrow Bones* and *The Wanton Seed* included short biographies of Gardiner and the Hammonds. Since we will be re-issuing both books, it makes sense to avoid unnecessary repetition; for this edition, then, we have replaced those short pieces with more detailed ones, extracted from Frank Purslow's longer articles in Volume I of the *Folk Music Journal*. It also seemed fitting to include a piece on Frank himself, and this has been written for us by Derek Schofield, based on interviews conducted in 2006.

Biographies: the Singers

In *Classic English Folk Songs*, EFDSS's revised re-issue of *The Penguin Book of English Folk Songs*, a section was devoted to biographical information on the singers from whom the songs were noted. There was a relatively small number of individuals involved there, however; the total for *Marrow Bones* is far greater, and considerations of both time and space have led us to decide to concentrate, to begin with, on introductory matter and bibliography. This will allow us to devote proper attention to the singers in the second, companion volume, *The Wanton Seed*. Many of them are represented in both books.

Bibliographies

A general bibliography, compiled by David Atkinson, appeared in *Classic English Folk Songs*; and a much more extensive one is available at the EFDSS website. For *Marrow Bones*, we have concentrated on two areas: publications which feature material from the Hammond and Gardiner collections and from the areas they worked in, and books and articles relating to the Broadside press; the latter compiled by David Atkinson with some selected internet resources also listed. Although the folk song collectors of the early twentieth century were mostly well aware that many of the songs they were hearing had been printed (sometimes in almost identical words) on the cheap song-sheets sold by nineteenth-century publishers like Pitts and Catnach in London, and by others in most parts of Britain and Ireland into the early years of the twentieth century, many were inclined to dismiss these as mere commercialised corruptions of the real songs of the folk.

Although it is certainly true that the broadside press took material from oral tradition (and everywhere else it could find anything that might sell) it is beyond doubt that the bulk of songs found in tradition derive, at least textually, from broadsides and similar cheap print publications. Gardiner, for one, was pragmatic about this, and got his colleague J F Guyer to spend time at the British Museum looking for broadside texts that might explain puzzling words or lines; but others were more inclined to sweep the whole business under the carpet, with the result that to this day many people with a strong interest in folk music don't appreciate the absolutely fundamental role of cheap print in its transmission and, frequently, origination. Frank Purslow emphasised this point in his books and is, if anything, even more convinced of it now; as are we.

To conclude, we have both derived enormous interest and enjoyment from the job of preparing this influential and much-loved collection for a new readership, and the opportunity it has presented of exploring some of the complexities of the extensive manuscript archive on which the book is based. It is our hope that singers and musicians, whether they are encountering the songs here for the first time or re-visiting old friends, will discover or re-discover things that they will want to sing themselves and make part of their own lives, as they were part of the lives of the men and women who sang them to Gardiner and the Hammonds a century ago. They speak to the human condition today just as they did then.

Malcolm Douglas
Sheffield, April 2007

Steve Gardham
Hull, April 2007

Dr George Gardiner
Photograph reproduced from *Folk Music Journal* vol I number
3, 1967, where it was printed with the permission of
Mr B A Stenhouse, Registrar of the Edinburgh Academy.

DR GEORGE GARDINER

GEORGE Barnet Gardiner was born at Kincardine-on-Forth, Perthshire in 1852 or early 1853, the fifth of six children. At the time, his father, who like his mother was a native of Milnathort, Kinross-shire, was minister to the parish of Tulliallan.

After graduating with an MA degree from Edinburgh University, where he had distinguished himself in classical subjects, he became assistant to Professors Blackie and Butcher at the university. In October 1883 he was appointed to the staff of the Edinburgh Academy as classics master, a post he held until 1896. In 1890 Henry Hammond ... joined the staff at the Academy. Although also a classics master Hammond's interests were much wider than Gardiner's – he was a first-class athlete and sportsman and professed to be more interested in Continental methods of education than in the classics which he nevertheless taught with great enthusiasm – but the two men shared an intense interest in folk song and became close friends.

Gardiner had had this interest in folk song for many years, originally that of his native Scotland, but in the course of his visits to the Continent he gradually extended his range of interest and, in 1903, he 'entered on the systematic study of the folk-songs of Europe, learning typical examples of ancient French, German, Russian, Swedish, Finnish, Hungarian and even Bohemian and Slovenian songs'.[1] It then occurred to him that England might have such songs and, on hearing of its existence, he immediately became a member of the Folk-Song Society, obtaining the six issues of the Journal published up to that date, together with all the published collections then available. 'In these volumes I at last found what I wanted – a body of nameless, hereditary English songs of the people comparable to songs published in the Swedish collection of Geyer and Afzelius, the Manx collection (ed. W H Gill – F.P.), the Balmoral collection of Scotch songs and the Hungarian collection of Matrai Gabriel.'[2]

The first English song appearing in Gardiner's note-books is a version of 'Jones' Ale' noted, together with about twenty others, in the Bath area some time in 1904. Despite his extensive knowledge of folk song and of music in general, Gardiner did not trust himself to note down tunes correctly, so this first batch of songs was probably noted in collaboration with Hammond ... whose home was at Clevedon a few miles away. Early in 1905 Gardiner and Hammond were staying at Minehead and resolved 'to collect some of the gleanings of Mr Sharp's harvest'.[3] With the help of two local musicians, E Quintrell of Helston and C S Parsonson of Launceston, Gardiner started work in the St Ives area, noting twenty-six songs during May and February of that year. In June he noted a few songs in the Milverton area of Somerset with Hammond. One or two of these early 'gleanings' were printed in No. 7 of the *Journal of the Folk-Song Society* (1905).

About this time Miss Lucy Broadwood, then Secretary of the Folk-Song Society, suggested to Gardiner that he turn his attention to the largely unexplored territory of Hampshire[4] where Balfour Gardiner, the composer – no relation – whose home was at Sutton Scotney, had promised help in noting tunes. During June 1905 Gardiner and his new collaborator noted about sixty songs in the areas of Twyford, Cheriton, Hursley, Ropley and Itchen Abbas, but the haymaking season, followed closely by the harvest, brought their work to a halt. The country people were either too busy or too tired to sing. From January to March 1906 Gardiner was again staying at Bath with Hammond and they noted about 100 songs in the vicinity. After this, Hammond, again at Miss Broadwood's suggestion, started work on his Dorset collection with the help of his brother Robert, and Gardiner returned to Hampshire.

Enlisting the help of two more local musicians, Charles Gamblin of Winchester and John Fisher Guyer of Southampton, Gardiner started work in earnest. This time when the haymaking season arrived he turned his attention to the workhouses 'where singers can be had at any time'.[5] By November he had noted about another 450 songs. The next year (1907) between May and November he added another 440. From the evidence of his note-books it appears that his method of working was perhaps unique, albeit probably dictated by circumstances. As the work of collection proceeded it is obvious that the musicians rarely, if ever, accompanied Gardiner on his expeditions. A list of songs known by each singer was noted together with whatever texts Gardiner was able to obtain, or was interested in noting in full. Later – presumably when one of his collaborators had some free time – the note-book was handed over to a musician who revisited the singers and noted the tunes.

This method of working becomes increasingly obvious as time goes on: in January 1909 Gamblin was noting tunes to songs Gardiner had taken down the previous September. Later still the time gap increases with the inevitable melancholy note 'singer gone'. This is almost certainly the reason why no songs noted after the end of 1907 were ever sent to the Society. In his spare time, presumably during the winter months, Gardiner was arranging for all the songs he thought worth preserving to be copied, and regular 'budgets' were sent to Miss Broadwood. Because of the time lag in noting the tunes and the time spent in the actual copying, Gardiner was well over twelve months behind his actual collecting when he sent his last batch of songs in 1909. Of approximately 1,100 songs collected up to December 1907 Gardiner copied about 800. That there were another 600-odd songs remaining in his note-books, which Gardiner either had not wished or never had the chance to copy, seems to have escaped attention until I came across them fifty years later.

It cannot be stated with any certainty when Gardiner actually ceased his collecting activities. He continued visiting various workhouses (including the Portsmouth Workhouse and Infirmary where he noted a fair number of sea songs and shanties from ex-seamen) right through 1908 and possibly into 1909, adding altogether another 320 songs to his collection. The bulk of these are from Hampshire, but there are about fifty from the bordering areas of Surrey and Sussex and 17 from Wiltshire 'Unions'. J F Guyer noted the last tunes in August 1909.

[Gardiner died on 19 January 1910, of kidney failure; which, judging by his frequent stays at the Waverley Hydropathic Establishment, Melrose, had been impending for some time.][6] He was buried in Warriston Cemetery, Edinburgh. After his death, his note-books, together with the original music manuscripts of Quintrell, Parsonson, Hammond, Gamblin, Guyer, Balfour Gardiner and Duncan Hume (who sent Gardiner a few songs from Bournemouth) came into the possession of the Folk-Song Society.

Frank Purslow

[1] *The Edinburgh Academy Chronicle*, May 1910.
[2] Letter to the *Hampshire Chronicle*, 1 September 1906.
[3] Letter from Henry Hammond to Miss Lucy Broadwood, 2 June 1905.
[4] In actual fact Miss Broadwood herself had done a little collecting in the area. Miss Alice Gillington also did some collecting in Hampshire, but at a date unknown.
[5] Article in the *Hampshire Chronicle*, 20 February 1909.
[6] Information supplied by Bob Askew, 2007.]

The above is extracted from Frank Purslow's article, 'The George Gardiner Folk Song Collection', in *Folk Music Journal*, vol I, number 3, 1967, 129–57.

HENRY AND ROBERT HAMMOND

THE large collection of field note-books, tune books and manuscript copies known as the 'Hammond Collection' is the result of about four years' intensive work by two brothers, Henry and Robert Hammond, the majority of it undertaken in Dorset. Most of the correspondence between them and the Folk-Song Society was carried on by Henry and, as a result, it is Henry's name which has, unjustly, become almost solely associated with the manuscripts and the various published collections taken from them. In fact the burden of noting the songs was shared almost equally, Robert noting the texts and Henry the tunes.

Henry Edward Denison Hammond was born at Priston, Somerset in 1866 and Robert Francis Frederick Hammond also at Priston in 1868. They were the second and third sons of Henry Walmsley Hammond, son of the Revd John Hammond, and Catherine Mary, daughter of the Revd Samuel Wyatt Cobb, rector of Ightham, Kent. Their father was an old Etonian who had retired prematurely from HM Bengal Civil Service owing to ill-health.

Regarding Henry's education and early career I cannot do better than quote from the obituary article in *The Edinburgh Academy Chronicle*, June 1910:

Mr Hammond was educated at Lancing College; from there he went in 1886 with an open scholarship to Corpus Christi College, Oxford ... Straight from Oxford he went for a year to Blairlodge School, and in October 1890 he joined the staff of the Edinburgh Academy; and he may fairly be said at once to have become one of its most distinguished members ... He was an interesting and stimulating teacher, keenly anxious to get the best out of his pupils, and sparing no efforts to attain that result ... In spite of his expressed depreciation of the Classics, Mr Hammond was a polished and tasteful classical scholar; he also acquired a first rate acquaintance with French and German; he was thoroughly well-read in the best, and in some of the out-of-the-way English literature; lastly he had studied the theory of education more than most practical schoolmasters, and to greater advantage than most theorists ... It was this work that led to his leaving the Academy ... in 1899 he was appointed Director-General of Education in Rhodesia...

After only twelve months in his Rhodesian post Henry suffered a severe breakdown in health from which he never fully recovered. The effects of the enforced semi-idleness caused by his ill-health must have been all the more galling to one of such an active nature. [He had been an enthusiastic athlete and sportsman.] Maybe it was this that led him to the collection of folk songs, for here was something that was useful and would enable him to be 'out and about', without having to adhere to a strict schedule.

It was presumably at the Academy that Henry first met Dr George Gardiner, and may have caught the enthusiasm for folk song from him. [It is also worth noting that the Revd Charles Marson and Cecil Sharp were friends of the Hammond family.] The two men apparently became close friends and spent a lot of time in each other's company. Gardiner was in Bath in 1904 and noted some songs there and it is most likely that Hammond collaborated in this instance. It was whilst staying at Minehead early in 1905 that the idea of collecting on a serious scale seems to have entered their heads.

Despite enquiries directed to Robert's only surviving relative I have so far been unable to obtain any information regarding his early years or subsequent career. The eldest brother, Anthony, is survived by a daughter, Miss Cecily Hammond, who has very kindly given me what information she has concerning her uncles; about Robert, however, she knows very little. The photograph of the brothers was also provided by Miss Hammond and is reproduced with her permission.

The Hammonds' attempts at 'trying to collect some of the gleanings of Mr Sharp's harvest'[1] bore immediate fruit. Dr Gardiner had to leave temporarily for Cornwall (where he forthwith started his own collecting activities), so the brothers decided to proceed on their own. Their first 'finds' were at Combe Florey, West Somerset: Mrs Gulliver, from whom they noted forty-three songs, and Amos Ash who gave them thirteen.[2] By this time Dr Gardiner had rejoined them and the total Somerset yield was eighty-three songs. Letters which Henry wrote to Miss Lucy Broadwood dated 2nd (two), 5th and 9th June 1905 give some information concerning the singers and the methods employed in collecting the songs:

My brother has been indefatigable in hunting up singers; I have done most of the transcribing and noting of the words and have made a few notes and suggestions upon them, not in a spirit of presumption, for your edification, but rather for my own pleasure. I have also been bold enough to take down a few tunes, most of which I have submitted to Mr Jeboult for revision as to time. I am not musician enough to be up to all the intricacies of time but have a good ear and can take down, even if rather laboriously, the right notes and give them their right value ... Dr Gardiner's liberality provided the services of Mr H A Jeboult, organist of St Mary's, Taunton, who spared no pains in taking down the tunes according to the F.S. Society's instructions.[3] He is a very nice man to work with and keen on folk songs ... In justice to him I have always put my initials after every tune on which I tried my less practised hand ... I have written out the songs exactly as I heard them with no attempts at Bowdlerisms or expurgation. I thought it best upon reflection to treat the songs just as the tunes, though it is of course clear that a certain number of verses are quite unprintable.

At Miss Broadwood's suggestion the brothers then turned their attention to the virgin territory of Dorset where, during the months of August, September and October 1905 they noted a further 193 songs. By this time Henry (probably with encouragement from Miss Broadwood) had lost his feelings of inadequacy regarding musical notation and from then on all the tunes were noted by him whilst Robert concentrated on the texts.

Apart from Henry's introduction to the selection of songs published in the Folk-Song Society's Journal in 1907, neither of the Hammonds seems to have ever made any public statements regarding their activities, the material they collected, or their attitude towards English folk song in general. Unlike Dr Gardiner, it is doubtful if they made a close study of the songs they noted. Their attitude seems to have been that they were doing their job to the best of their ability and that it was up to people more qualified than they to pass judgement on the results. This does not mean that they could not discern a folk song when they heard it. There is almost nothing among their songs that is in any way worthless and, in fact, their MSS contain versions of interesting and important songs never, or rarely, noted by other collectors at that time.

The last batch of songs was forwarded (to Miss Broadwood) on November 27th 1906, making a total of 412 songs. Although Henry was to live for another 3½ years no more were ever submitted to the Folk-Song Society; the reason for that I have been unable to discover. [...] The total number of tunes noted was 648. [There were] 236 songs not sent to the Folk-Song Society, plus 270 texts without tunes ... the exceptionally large number of texts noted without tunes is puzzling. Do they represent work done by Robert on his own, probably when Henry was indisposed, or – which I find more likely – did Henry consider that the tunes (probably Ionian) would be considered too uninteresting by the members of the Folk-Song Society?[4]

Henry apparently retained his interest in sports and games until the end. In June 1910 he attended the Amateur Golf Championship at Hoylake. The result was another attack of influenza from which he seemed to recover; but on 8th June he was taken ill with pneumonia and his condition soon became critical. He died on the evening of Thursday, 16th June 1910, and was buried in Edinburgh.

Robert remained a member of the Folk-Song Society until at least 1921. I have been unable to discover the exact date or circumstances of his death. Henry died a bachelor, but Robert married and is survived by his only child, a daughter. The Hammonds' MSS eventually came into the possession of Dr Vaughan Williams, who presented them to the English Folk Dance and Song Society.

Frank Purslow

[1] Letter to Miss Lucy Broadwood, 2 June 1905.
[2] These two singers, and one or two more in the area, were later visited by Cecil Sharp in September 1980. He refers to Mrs Gulliver as [Mrs Jane] 'Gulliford'. (Sharp may have been right: although the 1901 census records no Gullifords at Combe Florey – and there is a Jane Gulliver, aged thirty-eight – many years later Peter Kennedy recorded a Reg Gulliford, apparently her son.)
[3] The Folk-Song Society, in its early days, published a leaflet, price 1½d, of hints to would-be collectors. It is perhaps to this that Henry Hammond refers.
[4] This is borne out by Henry's attitude to 'The Banks of Sweet Primroses' – 'which were so numerous we did not stop to gather any'.

The above is extracted from Frank Purslow's article, 'The Hammond Brothers' Folk Song Collection', in *Folk Music Journal*, vol I, number 4, 1968, 236–66.

The Hammond Brothers
Left to right: Robert and Henry Hammond.
Photograph by Crowe & Rodgers, Stirling.
Reproduced from *Folk Music Journal* vol I
number 4, 1968, where it was printed with the
permission of Miss Cecily Hammond.

FRANK PURSLOW

FRANK Purslow's enthusiasm for the Hammond and Gardiner collections was sparked in the 1950s by the EFDSS Librarian, Sara Jackson, who knew of his interest in ballad sheets of the eighteenth and nineteenth centuries. Very few people even knew of the existence of the manuscripts in the Library, but Frank offered to index the songs, starting with the Hammond collection.

When he turned to the much larger Gardiner collection, Frank found that most of the texts had not been copied out of the original notebooks, so the process of indexing also included typing out the texts.

As a result of his work, Frank Purslow contributed two important articles on George Gardiner and the Hammond brothers to the *Folk Music Journal*, in 1967 and 1968 respectively.

Meanwhile, Frank had become immersed in the emerging folk song revival of 1950s London. Growing up in Birmingham before the Second World War, he particularly liked folk songs and read Sharp's books and biography. His brother was already playing the guitar and singing, and his 78rpm records of Ewan MacColl and A L Lloyd led Frank to MacColl's 'Ballads and Blues' club in London in the mid-fifties. It was there that Frank heard his first traditional singer, Phoebe Smith, whom he visited at her home in Woodbridge in Suffolk. He also befriended Harry Cox, after meeting him on a rare visit to sing in London, and visited some of the old singers who were living in the Three Bridges area of Sussex.

Frank was a regular at The Ceilidhe Club at Cecil Sharp House where Peter Kennedy was introducing traditional singers and musicians to young folk enthusiasts. Soon, Frank was running two folk clubs himself, helped by the guitarist John Pearse. In 1959, Frank and John recorded a record for Dobell's label: entitled *Rap-a-tap-tap*, it comprised traditional songs from the Hammond, Gardiner and Sharp collections, and was also released in the States with the colourful, if rather misleading, title *Unexpurgated Songs of Erotica*.

Because of his knowledge, Frank was approached by Peter Kennedy who wanted to produce cheap song books for the growing number of folk club singers. The song book was to be a joint publication between the EFDSS and the publishers Chappell's.

Frank recalled, 'I put together a hundred songs and they started to have qualms about some of the texts, which they thought were too risqué. But we pointed out that the equally risqué collection, *The Idiom of the People* had been published in 1958 without anyone complaining. So *Marrow Bones* eventually appeared in 1965 and was followed by three more books.' They were *The Wanton Seed* (1968), *The Constant Lovers* (1972) and *The Foggy Dew* (1974).

By the time the books were published, Frank had moved to live in Bampton in Oxfordshire, home of the famous morris dancers. Reg Hall, whom he had met at the Ceilidhe Club, had shown him how to play the melodeon, and encouraged him to visit the traditional morris sides. Frank first went to Abingdon, where he got on well with the dancers, ending up fooling for them on Mayor's Day in about 1958. In 1960, Frank was in Abingdon the weekend before Whitsun and walked over to Bampton to see the morris squire, Francis Shergold, who was lamenting the fact that he had no musician. Frank recommended Reg Hall, who had already visited Bampton and knew the tunes. Reg has played for Bampton ever since.

Soon after, Frank moved out of London to live in Bampton, where he played and danced at different times with both Francis Shergold's and Arnold Woodley's morris sides. He also taught several local young dancers to play, particularly fiddler Matthew Green (now squire of the third team in Bampton and a member of Woodpecker Band and Magpie Lane) and Alastair Cook who is a fine melodeon player. Frank formed his own local band, Morris Eight, later the Bampton Barn Dance Band, which became extremely popular in the area.

Frank continued to live in retirement in Bampton. Not so involved now in either folk music or morris dancing, he nevertheless maintained a lively interest in the dancing in Bampton. His musical interests were extensive and he was extremely knowledgeable about English classical music. In recognition of his contribution to folk song, dance and music, Frank was awarded the English Folk Dance and Song Society's Gold Badge in 2007.

Derek Schofield

Frank Purslow

Frank Purslow died suddenly in the early hours of Wednesday 25 April 2007; he was 81. We dedicate this new edition of *Marrow Bones* to his memory.

ACKNOWLEDGEMENTS

MALCOLM Douglas revised *The Penguin Book of English Folk Songs* for reissue by EFDSS as *Classic English Folk Songs* in 2003. He maintains extensive websites for the South Riding Folk Arts Network, Yorkshire Folk Arts and the *Folk Music Journal*, and is graphic designer for *Stirrings* magazine (folk and acoustic music in the South Yorkshire/North Derbyshire region) and the Sheffield Folk Festival.

Steve Gardham compiles the 'Songs Under the Microscope' feature for *English Dance and Song* magazine and (as 'Dungbeetle') writes the series 'A Veritable Dungheap', examinations of the role of the broadside ballad in the evolution of folk song, which began in *EDS* and continues at the *Musical Traditions* website: http://www.mustrad.org.uk/. He is Chair of the Yorkshire Garland Group, which is preparing a web-based archive of traditional song in Yorkshire.

David Atkinson is editor of the *Folk Music Journal* and author of *The English Traditional Ballad: Theory, Method and Practice* (Aldershot and Burlington, VT: Ashgate, 2002). The third edition of his *English Folk Song: An Introductory Bibliography Based on the Holdings of the Vaughan Williams Memorial Library* (2006) is available on the EFDSS website. He is a member of the team preparing a critical edition of the James Madison Carpenter collection of traditional song, music, and drama, with special responsibility for textual editing.

Derek Schofield is editor of *English Dance and Song* and author of *The First Week in August: Fifty Years of the Sidmouth Festival* (Sidmouth International Festival, 2004). He has written biographies of William Kimber and Fred Jordan for the recent CDs, *Absolutely Classic: The Music of William Kimber* (EFDSS CD03, 1999) and *A Shropshire Lad* (Veteran VTD148CD, 2003).

Special thanks are due to

Malcolm Taylor, Librarian of the Vaughan Williams Memorial Library, and his colleagues Elaine Bradtke and Peta Webb, for their help with our explorations of the Hammond and Gardiner collections.

Steve Roud, for his invaluable Folk Song and Broadside indexes, and for kindly providing copies of some hard-to-find material.

Bob Askew and Tim Radford for sharing the results of their historical and genealogical researches.

Paul Sartin (of Faustus, Bellowhead and other bands) for help with technical musical issues, and for extensive information on Edith Sartin and her associates.

Frank Purslow, for the original *Marrow Bones* and for his unfailing patience and good humour when faced with our interminable questions on points of detail.

Vic Gammon, for a Foreword written at very short notice.

David Atkinson, for editorial advice, the broadside bibliography, and for making available to us his editing notes formulated for use on the Carpenter Collection.

The Songs

THE ASTROLOGER

Tune: Hammond D804. Marina Russell, Upwey, Dorset. January/February 1907.
Text: Hammond D630. Mr J Penny, Poole, Dorset. October 1906.

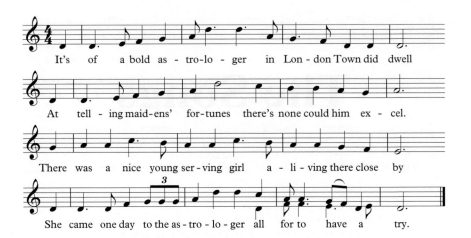

It's of a bold astrologer in London Town did dwell
At telling maidens' fortunes there's none could him excel.
There was a nice young serving girl a-living there close by
She came one day to the astrologer all for to have a try.

I hear that you tell fortunes, sir, would you tell me mine? said she.
Of course, my dear, without a doubt if you'll walk upstairs with me.
To walk upstairs with you, kind sir, I'm sure I am afraid.
She spoke it in such modesty as though she was a maid.

To walk upstairs with me, my dear, you need not be afraid
Knowing it was but the other day you with your master laid.
Then she began to curse and swear she would her master bring,
As witness for both him and her that it was no such thing.

My pretty maid, don't swear and curse, you'll make the deed the worse
For the crown piece that he gave to you, you've got it in your purse.
Oh indeed you can tell fortunes, sir, you've told me mine, said she
And out she pulled the crown piece. Good morning, sir! said she.

THE BIRD IN THE BUSH

Tune: Hammond D266. Robert Barratt, Piddletown, Dorset. September 1905.

Text: Hammond D68. William Poole, Taunton, Somerset. May 1905.

A fair maid a-milking did go
A fair maid a-milking did go.
Oh the wind did blow high and the wind did blow low
And it blew her pails to and fro.

She met with a man that she knew
She met with a man that she knew
And she boldly asked him if he'd got any skill
For to catch her a small bird or two.

Oh yes, I will show you some skill
And very good skill it be too
If you will come with me down to some shady tree
I will catch you a small bird or two.

So they went down together you shall see
Down under some green shady tree
And he fired at the bush and the bird did fly in
Just above of her lily-white knee.

Here's a health to the man and the maid
Here's a health to the bird in the bush
For we're all birds of one feather and we'll all flock together
Let the people say little or much.

Here's a health to the man and the maid
Here's a health to the jolly dragoon.
We've tarried here all day and drunk down the sun
Let's tarry here and drink down the moon.

THE BOLD FISHERMAN

Tune: Hammond S56. Mrs Gulliver (Gulliford), Combe Florey, Somerset. 1905.

Text: Hammond D106. George Roper (of Charlton St Mary), Blandford Union, Dorset.
August (?) 1905.

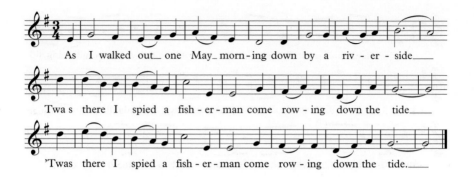

As I walked out one May morning down by a riverside
'Twas there I spied a fisherman come rowing down the tide
'Twas there I spied a fisherman come rowing down the tide.

Good morning to you, fisherman, how came you fishing here?
I'm fishing for my lady fair all down the river clear
I'm fishing for my lady fair all down the river clear.

'Twas then he rowed his boat to shore and tied it to a stake
And walked up to this lady fair her lily-white hand to take
And walked up to this lady fair her lily-white hand to take.

Then he pulled off his morning gown and laid it on the ground.
'Twas then she spied three chains of gold all round his neck was bound
'Twas then she spied three chains of gold all round his neck was bound.

Then she fell to her bended knees. Your pardon, sir, she cried,
For calling you a fisherman a-rowing on the tide
For calling you a fisherman a-rowing on the tide.

Rise up, rise up, my lady fair and don't down-daunted be
For not a word that you have said the least offended me
For not a word that you have said the least offended me.

I'll take you to my father's house and we will married be
And you shall have your fisherman to row you on the sea
And you shall have your fisherman to row you on the sea.

BOLD GENERAL WOLFE

Tune: Hammond D529. Sam Gregory, Beaminster, Dorset. July 1906.
Text: Hammond D174. William Bartlett, Wimborne Union, Dorset. December 1905.

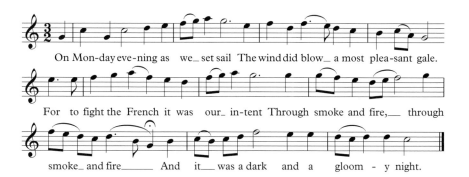

On Mon-day eve-ning as we set sail The wind did blow a most plea-sant gale.
For to fight the French it was our in-tent Through smoke and fire, through
smoke and fire And it was a dark and a gloom - y night.

On Monday evening as we set sail
The wind did blow a most pleasant gale.
For to fight the French it was our intent
Through smoke and fire, through smoke and fire
And it was a dark and a gloomy night.

Now the French was landed on the mountains high
And we poor hearts in the valleys lie.
Never mind, my lads, General Wolfe did say
Brave lads of honour, brave lads of honour
Old Engeland shall win the day.

Then the very first broadside we give to them
We killed seven hundred and fifty men.
Well done, my lads, General Wolfe did say
Brave lads of honour, brave lads of honour
Old Engeland shall win the day.

Then the very first broadside they give to us
They wounded our general in his right breast.
Then out of his tender breast loving blood did flow
Like any fountain, like any fountain
Till all his men were filled with woe.

Now here's a hundred guineas in bright gold
Take it and part it for my blood runs cold
And use your soldiers as you did before
Your soldiers own, your soldiers own
And they will fight for evermore.

And when to old Engeland you do return
Pray tell my friends that I am dead and gone.
Pray tell my tender old mother dear
That I am dead, o, that I am dead, o
And I shall never see her no more.

THE BOLD PRINCESS ROYAL

Gardiner H72. William Randall, Hursley, Hampshire. June 1905.

On the four-teenth of Feb-ru-a-ry we sailed from the land In the bold *Prin-cess Roy-al* bound for New-found-land With for-ty brave sea-men for our ship's com-pa-ny From the east-ward to the west-ward and so sail-ed we.

On the fourteenth of February we sailed from the land
In the bold *Princess Royal* bound for Newfoundland
With forty brave seamen for our ship's company
From the eastward to the westward and so sailed we.
> *With forty brave seamen for our ship's company*
> *From the eastward to the westward and so sailed we.*

On the eighteenth of February so fair blew the sky
When the man from our masthead a sail he did spy.
She came bearing down on us for to see what we were
And under her mizzen-peak black colours she wore.
> *She came bearing down on us, etc.*

Good Lord, cries our captain, what shall we do now?
Here comes a bold pirate to rob us, I know.
Oh no, cries our chief mate, that never can be so
We will shake out a reef, boys, and from her we'll go.
> *Oh no, cries our chief mate, etc.*

In time this bold pirate she hove alongside
With a loud-speaking trumpet, Whence come you? she cried.
Our captain being aft, my boys, he answered her so
We are come from fair London and are bound for Callao.
> *Our captain being aft, etc.*

Then back your main topsail and heave your ship to
For I have got some letters to send home by you.
I will back my main topsail and heave my ship to
But it will be in some harbour not alongside of you.
> *I will back up my main topsail, etc.*

They chased us to windward, they chased us that day
They chased us to windward but they could not make way.
They fired shots after us but none could prevail
For the bold *Princess Royal* soon showed them her tail.
> *They fired shots after us, etc.*

6

Thank God, cries our captain, now the pirates are gone
Go down to your grog, boys, go down everyone
Go down to your grog, boys and be of good cheer
For it's while we have sea-room, brave boys, never fear.
Go down to your grog, etc.

THE BOLD TROOPER

Gardiner H1286. Jesse Cole, Oakley, Hampshire. September 1908.

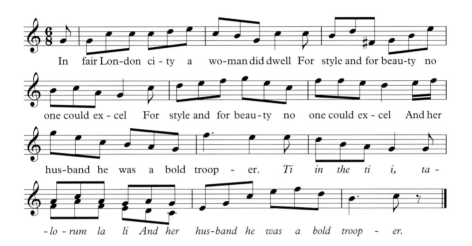

In fair Lon-don ci-ty a wo-man did dwell For style and for beau-ty no one could ex-cel For style and for beau-ty no one could ex-cel And her hus-band he was a bold troop - er. Ti in the ti i, ta - -lo - rum la li And her hus-band he was a bold troop - er.

In fair London city a woman did dwell
For style and for beauty no one could excel
For style and for beauty no one could excel
And her husband he was a bold trooper.

Chorus: *Ti in the ti i, talorum la li*
            And her husband he was a bold trooper.

There was an old tailor who lived there close by
And on this 'ere woman he casted his eye.
Ten guineas I'll give you this night for to lie
If your husband is out upon duty.

The bargain was made and they both went to bed
They hadn't been there long till they fell fast asleep
Then, Hide me! Oh hide me, the tailor he said
For I hear the bold knock of the trooper.

There's a three-cornered cupboard behind the room door
And there I will hide you so safe and secure
And there I will hide you so safe and secure
If you've heard the bold knock of the trooper.

She goes down the stairs for to welcome him in.
For your kisses and compliments I don't care a pin
For your kisses and compliments I don't care a pin.
Come light me a fire, said the trooper.

Dear husband, dear husband, there's no firestuff
We'll both go to bed and we'll feel warm enough
We'll both go to bed and we'll feel warm enough.
No! Come light me a fire, said the trooper.

There's a three-cornered cupboard behind the room door
And that I will burn so certain and sure
And that I will burn so certain and sure
So come light me a fire, said the trooper.

Dear husband, dear husband, that's not my desire
For to burn a good cupboard to light you a fire
For in it I keep a gamecock I admire.
Then I'll scare your gamecock, said the trooper.

He goes up the stairs and he opens the door
And there sat the tailor so safe and so sure.
He gave the cupboard a knock to the middle of the floor.
Is this your gamecock? said the trooper.

He put his hand in his pocket and pulled out his shears
And off on the table he cut his two ears,
Saying, For my night's lodging I've paid very dear.
And away ran the poor croppy tailor.

THE BONNY BUNCH OF ROSES O!

Gardiner H440. Charles Windebank, Lyndhurst, Hampshire. July 1906.

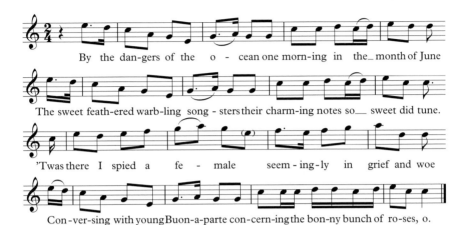

By the dan-gers of the o - cean one morn-ing in the month of June

The sweet feath-ered warb-ling song - sters their charm-ing notes so sweet did tune.

'Twas there I spied a fe - male seem - ing-ly in grief and woe

Con - ver-sing with young Buon-a-parte con-cern-ing the bon-ny bunch of ro-ses, o.

By the dangers of the ocean one morning in the month of June
The sweet feathered warbling songsters their charming notes so sweet did tune.
'Twas there I spied a female seemingly in grief and woe
Conversing with young Buonaparte concerning the bonny bunch of roses, o.

O mother, said young Napoleon, as he pressed his mother by the hand
Do, mother, pray, have patience until I'm able to command.
I will raise a terrible army and o'er the frozen realms I'll go
And in spite of all the universe I will gain the bonny bunch of roses, o.

O son, never speak so venturesome for in England are the hearts of oak
There's England, Ireland and Scotland, their unity has never been broke.
Now son, look at your father, in St. Helena his body lies low
And you might follow after so beware of the bonny bunch of roses, o.

For he took three hundred thousand men, likewise some kings to join his throng
Why he was so well provided, enough to sweep the world along
But when they came to Moscow they were overpowered by driving snow
And Moscow was a-blazing so they lost the bonny bunch of roses, o.

Now mother, adieu for ever for alas I'm on my dying bed
If I'd lived I might have been clever but now I droop my youthful head.
But whilst my bones do moulder and weeping willows over me grow,
The deeds of bold Napoleon will sting the bonny bunch of roses, o.

THE BONNY BUNCH OF RUSHES

Hammond D263. Robert Barratt, Piddletown, Dorset. September/October 1905.

Early one summer morning abroad as I did walk for sport
Down by some pleasant arbour where lovers oft-times did resort
Oh there I spied a fair maid to whom my thoughts was gone astray
With a bunch of rushes in her hand which she had a-gathered by the way.

I gently stepped up to her embracing her most tenderly
She kindly did rebuke me and said, Kind sir, don't make too free.
Don't think for to ill-use me because that I am poor and low
Don't break my bunch of rushes but loose me, sir, and let me go.

My dear, I'll not ill-use you nor I mean to you no injury
Come sit you down by the side of me beneath yon green and spreading tree
With the lovely larks and linnets shall be witness to our tale of love
To you I will prove constant, I swear by all the powers above.

Then so modestly she did consent and on the ground we both sit down
For fear of any moisture she spread beneath her cambric gown
Where the lovely larks and linnets were witness to our love till 'twas o'er
She said, Kind sir, don't tease me nor break my bunch of rushes more.

So now we are 'pon parting, pray when shall we both meet again?
He answered, In a few days. Oh then the clerk shall say, Amen!
So come all you gentle listeners if to those arbours you do go
Pray don't forget the answer to the maiden's bunch of rushes, o!

Oh the pretty little bunch of rushes, the neat little bunch of rushes, o!

The Bonny Labouring Boy

Hammond D220. Robert Barratt, Piddletown, Dorset. October 1905.

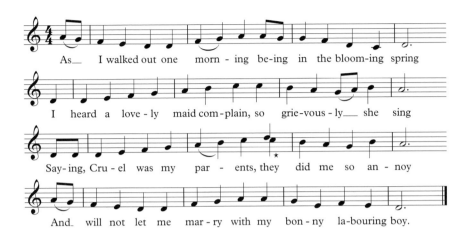

As__ I walked out one morn - ing be - ing in the bloom-ing spring

I heard a love - ly maid com -plain, so grie-vous - ly__ she sing

Say-ing, Cru - el was my par - ents, they did me so an - noy

And_ will not let me mar - ry with my bon - ny la-bouring boy.

As I walked out one morning, being in the blooming spring
I heard a lovely maid complain, so grievously she sing
Saying, Cruel was my parents, they did me so annoy
And will not let me marry with my bonny labouring boy.

Young Johnny was my true-love's name as you may plainly see
My parents did employ him their labouring boy to be
To harrow, reap, to sow the seed, to plough my father's land
And soon I fell in love with him as you may understand.

My father stepped up one morning and he seized me by the hand
He swore he'd send young Johnny unto some foreign land.
He locked me in my bedroom, my comfort to annoy
And to keep me there to weep and mourn for my bonny labouring boy.

My mother stepped up next morning, these words to me did say
Your father has intended to appoint your wedding day.
But I did not make no answer nor I dared not complain
But until I wed my labouring boy then single I'll remain.

Oh his cheeks are like the roses, his eyes as black as sloes
He smiles in his behaviour wherever my love goes.
He's manly, neat and handsome, his skin as white as snow
In spite of my parents with my labouring boy I'll go.

So fill this glass up to the brim, let the toast come early round
Here's a health to the labouring boy that ploughs and sows the ground
And when his work is over, his home he will enjoy
Oh how happy is the girl that weds with a bonny labouring boy.

THE BOYS OF KILKENNY

Tune and text: Hammond D575. Jim Burrows, Sherbourne Gravel Pits, Dorset, July 1906.

Text: Hammond D272. Mr T Hunt, Sherbourne Workhouse, Dorset, September 1905.

Fare you well to old Ireland, since I must leave the shore
And perhaps never see that little island no more
Leaving brothers and sisters and mother to mourn
And all for the sake of their dear darling son.

Oh there is one thing that do grieve my heart sore
That's to go and leave that charming pretty girl I adore.
But there is one thing more still runs in my mind
That's to think I should leave Kilkenny behind.

Kilkenny is a fine place, it lies in the west
And the more I think on it lies in my breast.
But now I am in London so far from my home
In Kilkenny I've a true love but here I have none.

My true-love was handsome, my true-love was fair
With her head of gold ringlets there's none can compare.
Oh her cheeks were like the red, red rose and her lips much the same
And her bosom like strawberries covered in cream.

The boys of Kilkenny are stout-hearted blades
And all their delight is in courting young maids
For they kiss them and they court them and they spend their money free
Of all the towns in Ireland, Kilkenny for me.

THE BREWER LADDIE

Hammond D341. George Bowditch, Charmouth, Dorset. March 1906.

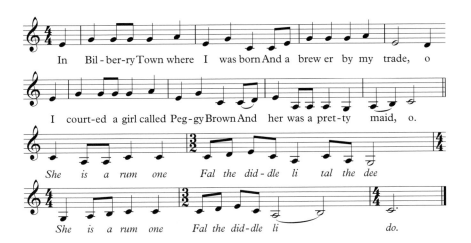

In Bilberry Town where I was born
And a brewer by my trade, o
I courted a girl called Peggy Brown
And her was a pretty maid, o.

Chorus: *She is a rum one*
Fal the diddle li tal the dee
She is a rum one
Fal the diddle li do.

Seven long years I courted her
All for to gain her favour
But along came a chap from Bilberry Town
And he swore that he would have her.

Will you go with me, my pretty maid
Will you go with me, my honey?
Oh yes, I'll go along with you
Although I'm promised to Johnny.

I did go to her mammy's house
Enquiring for my honey
So scornfully her old man replied
I ain't see'd her since Sunday.

Now her's a-gone so let her go
No more shall her a-grieve me.
I'm a young man free as you can see
And a little will relieve me.

THE BRICKLAYER'S DREAM

Tune and text (verse 1): Gardiner H747. Daniel Wigg, Preston Candover, Alresford, Hampshire. July 1907.

Text: Hammond G314. Unidentified singer; presumed Gloucestershire.

A bricklaying boy coming home from his work
A young damsel appeared in his sight.
O Sally love, said he, come and sit you down by me
And I'll tell you what I dreamt about last night
And I'll tell you what I dreamt about last night.

She came to a full stop with a smile on her cheeks
She came to a full stop saying, No!
I am going down for the cow and I cannot stay now
So I pray you, young man, let me go
So I pray you, young man, let me go.

Oh they both sat down together 'neath a green shady tree
Where the green leaves they are pleasant to be seen
And what they done there she never would declare
But she had the contents of his dream
But she had the contents of his dream.

Then they both went off together the cow for to fetch
And so nimbly tripped over the plain.
She said, My Jimmy sweet, the next time that we do meet
You may tell me your dream over again
You may tell me your dream over again.

THE BRISK YOUNG BUTCHER

Tune: Hammond S280. George Hatherill, Bath, Somerset. January 1906.
Text: Hammond D217. Alfred Scannell, Mere Workhouse, Dorset. 1905.

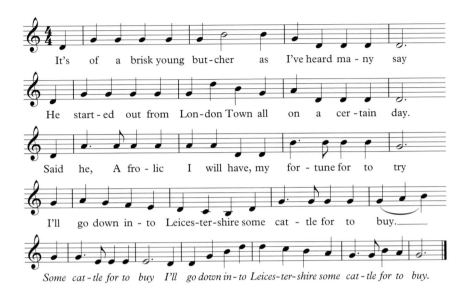

It's of a brisk young butcher as I've heard many say
He started out from London Town all on a certain day.
Said he, A frolic I will have, my fortune for to try
I'll go down into Leicestershire some cattle for to buy.
> *Some cattle for to buy*
> *I'll go down into Leicestershire some cattle for to buy.*

When he arrove in Leicestershire he stopped at an inn
He called for liquors of the best, his business to begin
He called for liquors of the best and being a roving blade
He presently did fix his eye upon the chambermaid.
> *Upon the chambermaid, etc.*

When the day was over, the night being coming on
The butcher came back to the inn his business being done.
He called for his supper, his reckoning left unpaid
Said he, This night I'll put a trick upon the chambermaid.
> *Upon the chambermaid, etc.*

When she took the candle to light him up to bed
When he come into the room, these words to her he said
One sovereign I will give to thee for to enjoy your charms
So all that night the fair maid slept all in the butcher's arms.
> *All in the butcher's arms, etc.*

He got up in the morning and prepared to go away
The landlady said, Kind sir, your reckoning you did not pay.
Oh no, the butcher he replied, oh do not think it strange
One sovereign I gave to your maid but did not get the change.
But did not get the change, etc.

Just in twelve months after, he came that way again
And just as he had done before, he stopped at the inn.
And soon the buxom chambermaid she chanced for him to spy
And brought the babe just three months old and placed it on his knee.
And placed it on his knee, etc.

The butcher sat like one amazed and at the child did stare
And when the joke it was found out how he did stamp and swear.
Kind sir, the chambermaid did say, Oh do not think it strange
One sovereign you did give to me and I have brought your change.
And I have brought your change, etc.

The company laughed, the maid did joke and flew in bliss around
And soon the tidings of the same spread all through Leicester Town.
The butcher was to justice brought who happened to live near
One hundred pounds he did pay down before he could get clear.
Before he could get clear, etc.

So all you brisk young butchers, a warning take by me
Look well into your bargain before you money pay
Or else maybe your folly will give you cause to range
For if you sport with a dandy lass, be sure you'll get the change.
Be sure you'll get the change, etc.

THE CAPTAIN'S APPRENTICE

Tune and text: Hammond D593. Edith Sartin, Corscombe, Dorset. July 1906.
Additional text: Hammond D548. George House, Beaminster, Dorset. June 1906.

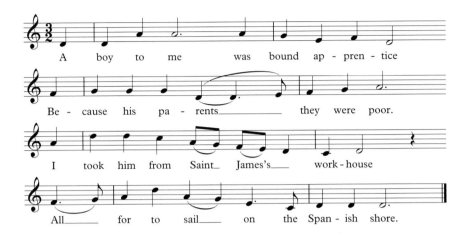

A boy to me was bound apprentice
Because his parents they were poor.
I took him from Saint James's workhouse
All for to sail on the Spanish shore.

A boy to me was bound apprentice
Because his parents they were poor.
I took him from Saint James's workhouse
All for to sail on the Spanish shore.

This boy one day he did offend me.
Nothing to him then did I say
But straightway to my yardarm I dragged him
And I kept him there till the very next day.

His hands and feet they hung towards me
His arms and legs hung down likewise
And with my tarry, tarry rope I killed him
Because I would not hear his cries.

And then my men they did reject me
Because that I had done such wrong
And in my cabin they close confined me
And bound me down in irons strong.

To London Town they then did bring me
And here lay I condemned to die
If I had by my men been ruled
I might have saved the poor boy's life and mine.

You captains bold that sail down the ocean
That have got servants to wait on thee
I pray you never, never ill-use them
For you plainly see 'twas the death of me.

A Child's Calendar

Gardiner H1044. Samuel Gray, Hartley Wintney Workhouse, Hampshire. October 1907.

Jan - u - ar - y   brings the snow   Makes our feet and   fin - gers glow.

January brings the snow
Makes our feet and fingers glow.

February brings the rain
Thaws the frozen lake again.

March brings breezes loud and shrill
Stirs the dancing daffodil.

April brings the primrose sweet
Scatters daisies at our feet.

May brings flocks of pretty lambs
Skipping by their fleecy dams.

June brings tulips, lilies, roses
Fills the children's hands with posies.

Hot July brings cooling showers
Apricots and gillyflowers.

August brings the sheaves of corn
And our harvest time is born.

Warm September brings the fruit
Sportsmen then begin to shoot.

Fresh October brings the pheasant
Then to gather nuts is pleasant.

Dull November brings the blast
Then the leaves are whirling fast.

Chill December brings the sleet
Blazing fire at Christmas treat.

Colin's Ghost

Hammond Wr303. Mrs Webb, King's Norton, Worcestershire. February 1906.

My   mam - my and   dad - dy   they   lived   in   a   cot   They

bought me a horse that could am - ble and trot And each mar - ket day__ it

fell to my share__ To go to the mar - ket with eggs and such ware.

With eggs and such ware__ To go to the mar - ket with eggs and such ware.

18

My mammy and daddy they lived in a cot
They bought me a horse that could amble and trot
And each market day it fell to my share
To go to the market with eggs and such ware.
With eggs and such ware
To go to the market with eggs and such ware.

Scarce seventeen summers were over my head
When over and around our gay village was spread
There was not a lane for a mile at the most
Was haunted by something they said was a ghost.
They said was a ghost, etc.

My mammy she never once scrupled to swear
She'd often seen ghosts and she knew what they were
So she spoke to my father, for he ruled the roast
To go in my place lest I should meet the ghost.
Lest I should meet the ghost, etc.

Being baulked of my ride I was vexed in my mind
And being resolved was the secret to find
So I peeped out of doors and saw a clear coast
Then off down the lane to discover the ghost.
To discover the ghost, etc.

Then who should I meet come sauntering along
But Colin the shepherd a-singing a song.
He sung it so sweet as he leaned on the post
He beckoned, I went, for I knew him no ghost.
For I knew him no ghost, etc.

With his arms round my waist he so eagerly pressed
I thought my poor heart would leap out of my breast.
He kissed my sweet lips till as warm as a toast
And so eagerly there I was pressed by the ghost.
I was pressed by the ghost, etc.

Being pleased with my fancy, I got home with speed
My mammy she never once missed me indeed.
Now instead of my supper, my tea and my toast
I nightly attend, well pleased with my ghost.
Well pleased with my ghost, etc.

THE COMFORT OF MAN

Tune and text: Gardiner H215. George Digweed, Micheldever, Hampshire. March 1906.

Text: Hammond D119. Henry Adams, Sturminster Newton, Dorset. 1905.

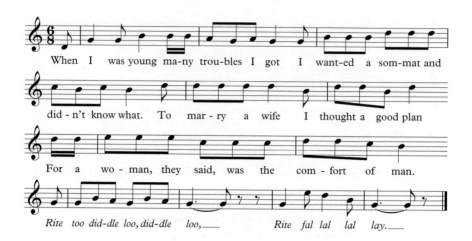

When I was young many troubles I got
I wanted a sommat and didn't know what.
To marry a wife I thought a good plan
For a woman, they said, was the comfort
    of man.

Chorus: *Rite too diddle loo, diddle loo,*
            Rite fal lal lal lay.

Miss Betsy, my sweetheart, she lived close by
I loved her a little and she liked I
So at length I sent her some sweet pretty
    letters
To tell her as how I could marry her betters.

When Miss Betsy read this she scoffed and she
    frowned
She said that her betters were not to be found.
And when she was through a-picking her hops
She came over the way and she slapped
    my chops.

I was ready to faint and fit for to cry
When a dab of fresh butter came slap in
    my eye.
But, says she, believe me I'll always be true
So go to the church I will with you.

We hadn't been married the best part of
    a week
And already her tongue begins to speak.
She broke my head with the frying pan
And soon I discovered the comfort
    of man.

Now Betsy she's in the family way
She does what she likes and I daresn't
    say nay.
Late the other night, as I wanted to doze
She bit a piece off the end of my nose.

Oh, Betsy, says I, what are you about?
You've cracked my head and disfigured
    my snout
And when that you bring me a son or a
    daughter
It'll have a long nose, for mine is the
    shorter.

At night when I goes home, sadly tired from
    my work
She opens the door and cries out like a Turk
Take this squalling young brat and get it
    to sleep
For all day long no peace would it keep.

I rue the day that ever I married
I wish that I had longer tarried.
I can never be happy, do all what I can
Oh Lord, what a plague is the comfort of man!

THE CROCKERY WARE

Tune and text: Gardiner H237. Isaac Hobbes, Micheldever, Hampshire. May 1906.
Text: Gardiner H626. Charles Hobbes, Easton, Winchester, Hampshire. September 1906.

In__ Mans-field Town there lived a spark He court-ed a girl both gay and smart.

He asked of__ her one_ fa-vour right If he could sleep with her one night.

To my right fol lol lol lid-dle lol the day, Right fol lol lol lid-dle lol the day.

In Mansfield Town there lived a spark
He courted a girl both gay and smart.
He asked of her one favour right
If he could sleep with her one night.

Chorus: *To my right fol lol lol liddle lol the day,*
           Right fol lol lol liddle lol the day.

Now this young girl she did contrive
How for to fix a joke that night
So on the landing she placed a chair
And on it put the crockery ware.

This young man rose in the middle of the night
Thinking to find his heart's delight.
He banged his shins against the chair
And upset the old woman's crockery ware.

The old woman rose in a terrible fright
And loudly she did call for a light.
Says she, Young man, how came you here
Capsizing of my crockery ware?

Miss Betsy lay in the very next room
A-laughing at the game going on.
Says she, Young man, I do declare
You must pay my mother for the crockery ware.

The bobby was sent for without delay
The money down I had to pay.
I paid three shillings I do declare
To buy the old woman a new crockery ware.

Come all you wild and rambling sparks
That loves to ramble in the dark
Don't bang your shins against a chair
Or upset the old woman's crockery ware.

Compliments Returned

Gardiner C7. Thomas Bennet, South Petherwin, Cornwall. February 1905.

Now, since you've called on me to sing I'll see what I can do
But I don't know what to sing about unless it be of you.
You've often said nice things of me and I'm sure what you say is true
So I'll just return the compliment and say what I think of you.

Chorus: *Folerol le diddle ol folerol le day*
                    Folerol le diddle ol folerol le day.

Now with this young man I will begin, as he is first in sight.
Pray, sir, where did you get the tin you're spending here tonight?
Your conscience pricks you, I've no doubt, but you know that it is true
That you've been and put something up the spout, so I don't think much of you.

Now there's a young man sitting here, I'm sure he's in disgrace.
Before he come in here tonight, he should have washed his face.
But soap, he says, is very dear, to buy it it won't do.
You think a great deal of yourself but I don't think much of you!

Now there's a young lady sitting here, I'm sure that I speak right
She never goes out with her young man but she stays out half the night.
Now you may laugh and wink at me but you know that it's all true.
Your mother, miss, she told me this, so I don't think much of you!

Now there's a couple sitting there, they make it a regular plan.
He talks to her so loving and says he's a single man.
But I tell you he's a married man and children has got two
His wife says he can't keep himself, so I'm sure he can't keep you!

But now I think I'll shut my trap and not say any more
But there's a young lady sitting there that I have seen before.
She says she wants to speak to me but what she wants I know
But I tell you, I'm a married man and I can't go home with you!

So now I think I'll say no more, by chance I make too free
And if I've tried to make you laugh, don't think the worse of me.
For it's all in jest what I have said and I don't think that it's true
And I hope you'll think as much of me as I have thought of you!

THE CROCODILE

Gardiner H347. Henry Lee, Whitchurch, Hampshire. May 1906.

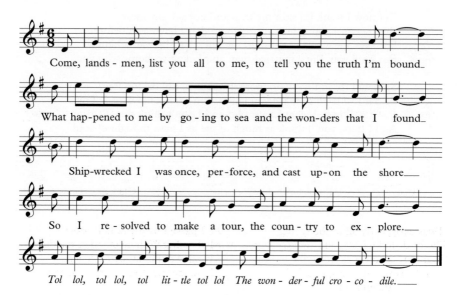

Come, lands-men, list you all to me, to tell you the truth I'm bound_

What hap-pened to me by go-ing to sea and the won-ders that I found_

Ship-wrecked I was once, per-force, and cast up-on the shore___

So I re-solved to make a tour, the coun-try to ex-plore.___

Tol lol, tol lol, tol lit-tle tol lol The won-der-ful cro-co-dile.___

Come, landsmen, list you all to me, to tell you the truth I'm bound
What happened to me by going to sea and the wonders that I found.
Shipwrecked I was once, perforce, and cast upon the shore
So I resolved to make a tour, the country to explore.

Chorus: *Tol lol, tol lol, tol little tol lol*
            The wonderful crocodile.

But far I'd not proceeded when alongside of the ocean
I saw something move about which I thought must be all the earth in motion.
But steering up close alongside I found 'twas a crocodile
And from his nose to the tip of his tail he measured five hundred mile.

This crocodile I could plainly see was not of a common race
I was obliged to climb up a very high tree before I could see his face.
Whilst up aloft the stem so high it blew a gale from the south
I lost my hold and away did fly right into the crocodile's mouth.

I travelled on for a month or two till I got into his maw
There I found of rum kegs not a few and a thousand bullocks in store.
Of life I banished all my care for in grub I wasn't stinted
And in this crocodile I lived ten years, very well contented.

This crocodile being very old, one day at last he died
But he was three years getting cold, he was so long and wide.
His skin was ten miles thick I'm sure, or very near about
For it took me full six months or more cutting a hole to get out.

So now once more I'd got on earth, resolved no more to roam
In a ship that passed I got a berth and now I'm safe at home.
And lest my story you should doubt, should you ever travel the Nile
Just where he fell you'll find the shell of the wonderful crocodile.

THE CROPPY BOY

Gardiner H975. Mrs Munday, Axford, Basingstoke, Hampshire. September 1907.

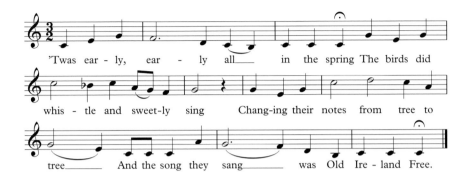

'Twas ear - ly, ear - ly all in the spring The birds did whis - tle and sweet-ly sing Chang-ing their notes from tree to tree And the song they sang was Old Ire - land Free.

'Twas early, early all in the spring
The birds did whistle and sweetly sing
Changing their notes from tree to tree
And the song they sang was Old
        Ireland Free.

It was early, early all in the night
The yeoman cavalry did me affright.
The yeoman cavalry was my downfall
And taken I was by the Lord Cornwall.

As I was going up Wexford Street,
My own first cousin I chanced to meet.
My own first cousin did me betray
For one fair guinea swore my life away.

My Lord Cornwall said he'd set me free
If I would tell on my comrades three.
Sooner than tell on my comrades three
I'd sooner die on the gallows tree.

It was in the guard-room where I
        was laid
And in the parlour where I was tried.
My sentence passed and courage low
And to a dungeon I was forced to go.

As I passed by my father's door
My brother William stood at the door.
My aged father stood there also
My tender mother her hair she tore.

My sister Mary heard of the express
She ran downstairs in her morning dress.
Five hundred guineas I will lay down
To see my brother safe through
        Wexford Town.

As I was going up Wexford Hill
Who could blame me to cry my fill?
I looked behind and I looked before
My tender mother I shall see no more.

As I was mounted on the scaffold high
My aged father did me deny.
My aged father did me deny
And the name he gave me was the
        Croppy Boy.

It was in Dungannon this young man died
And in Dungannon his body lies.
All you young people that do pass by
Pray shed a tear for the Croppy Boy.

THE CRUEL MOTHER

Hammond D863. Mrs Case, Sydling St Nicholas, Dorset. September 1907.

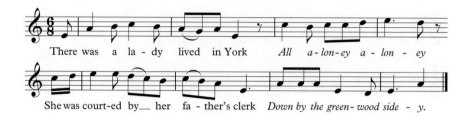

There was a lady lived in York
All aloney, aloney
She was courted by her father's clerk
Down by the greenwood sidey.

She leaned her back against an oak
But first it bent and then it broke.

She leaned herself against a thorn
And there she had two pretty babes born.

She had a penknife long and sharp
And she pressed it through their tender hearts.

She digged a grave both wide and long
And she buried them under a marble stone.

And she was sat at her father's hall
Oh there she saw two pretty babes playing at ball.

O babes, o babes, if you were mine
I would dress you up in the scarlet fine.

O mother, o mother, we once were thine
You did not dress us in the scarlet fine.

You digged a grave both wide and long
And buried us under a marble stone.

Babes, o babes, come tell to me
If you know what the future means to me.

Mother, o mother, you know right well
'Tis we for heaven and you for hell.

DEEP IN LOVE

Hammond D98. Jacob Baker, Bere Regis, Dorset. 1905.

Must I be bound or must I go free To love a young man who ne-ver loved me? Why should I act such a child-ish part To love a young man with all my heart?

Must I be bound or must I go free
To love a young man who never
              loved me?
Why should I act such a childish part
To love a young man with all my heart?

He loves another, he loves not me
And he cares not for my company.
He loves another, I'll tell you why
Because she's got more gold than I.

I put my back up against an oak
Thinking it was some trusty tree
But first it bent and then it broke
And so did my false love to me.

I put my hand into a bush
Thinking some sweeter flower
              to find.
I pricked my finger to the bone
Leaving that sweetest flower behind.

Since roses are such prickly flowers
They should be gathered when they're
              green
And I did court such an unkind love
I'm sure I'm striving against the stream.

And against the stream I dare not go
For fear that it should overflow
And not so deep in love am I
I care not whether he live or die.

He gave me honey all mixed with gall
He gave me words and vows withal.
He gave me a delicate gown to wear
All stitched with sorrow and hemmed
              with fear.

Now here's his health I mean to drink
And from his arms I will not shrink.
He hath my heart, go where he will
Although he is false, I must love him still.

THE DEVIL AND THE FARMER'S WIFE

Gardiner H267. Charles Gamblin, Winchester, Hampshire (no date).

There was an old man who lived near hell's gate *(whistle)*_____
_____ What hap - pened to him I soon will__ re - late.
With my *fal la la la lal,* *fal la lal la li day Fal la la la lal,* *fal la li day.*

There was an old man who lived near hell's gate
    (whistle)
What happened to him I soon will relate.

Chorus: *With my fal la la la lal, fal la lal la li day*
                Fal la lal lal, fal la li day.

The Devil he called upon him one day
One of your family I must take away.

This put the old man in a terrible fright
But good Mr Devil soon put him quite right.

It's not your eldest son I crave
But that damned scolding old bitch of a wife you have.

The Devil he took her up on his back
Just like a bold Scotsman carrying his pack.

The Devil he brought her close to hell's door
Get along in, you damned scolding old whore.

She saw some young devils all hanging in chains
She pulled off her pattens and dashed out their brains.

Some more little devils looked over the wall
Cried, Take her back, daddy, she'll murder us all.

So the Devil he cantered her over hell's wall
She landed on her arse, a hell of a fall.

Which proves that the women are worse than the men
If they go to hell they get thrown out again.

DICK TURPIN

Gardiner H453. George Smith, Fareham, Hampshire. July 1906.
Gardiner H1035. David Snugg, Hartley Wintney Workhouse, Hampshire. October 1907.

Dick Turpin, bold Dick, hie away! was the cry
And his pals were all startled, you'll guess
The pistols were levelled, the bullets whizzed by
As he leaped on the back of Black Bess.
Three officers mounted, led forward the chase
Resolved in my capture to share
But I smiled on their efforts to gain such a prize
As I leaped on the back of my mare.

Chorus: *Then while I've a bumper, what can I do less*
            Than in memory drink to my bonny Black Bess?
            Then while I've a bumper, what can I do less
            Than in memory drink to my bonny Black Bess?

Hark away! Hark away! Still onwards we press
And I saw by the glimmers of morn
Full many a mile on the back of Black Bess
That night I was gallantly borne.
High over, my Bet, thy fatigue thou must bear
Well cleared! Never falter for breath.
Hark forward, brave girl! My bonny black mare
We are speeding for life or for death.

When the spires of York Minster now burst on my view
And the chimes they were ringing a knell
Halt, halt, my brave mare, they no longer pursue
As she halted, she staggered, she fell
Her breathings are over, all hushed to her grave
My poor Black Bess once my pride
But her heart she had burst her rider to save
For Dick Turpin she lived and she died.

THE DOCKYARD GATE

Gardiner H868. Frederick Fennemore, Portsmouth Workhouse, Hampshire. August 1907.

Come all you mar-ried sea-men bold a few lines to you I'll write
Just to let you know how the game do go when you are out of sight
Just to let you know how the lads on shore go sport-ing with your wives
While you are on the roll-ing seas and ven-tur-ing your sweet lives.

Come all you married seamen bold a few lines to you I'll write
Just to let you know how the game do go when you are out of sight
Just to let you know how the lads on shore go sporting with your wives
While you are on the rolling seas and venturing your sweet lives.

It's now our ship she's outward bound and ready for to sail
May the heavens above protect my love with a sweet and pleasant gale
And keep him clear all from the shore and never more return
Until his pockets are well lined and then he's welcome home.

A last farewell she takes of him and she begins to cry
A-taking out her handkerchief to wipe her weeping eyes.
My husband's gone to sea, she cries, how hard it is my case
But still on shore there's plenty more, another will take his place.

Then she goes unto her fancy man, these words to him did say
My husband he is gone to sea, tomorrow is half-pay day
And you must wait at the dockyard gate until that I come out
For that very day we'll sweat his half-pay and drink both ale and stout.

That day they spent in sweet content till the half-pay was no more
Then, Never mind, my dear, she cries, he's working hard for more.
Perhaps he's at the masthead a-dying with the cold
Or perhaps he's at his watch on deck, our joys he can't behold.

And now our ship she's homeward bound, brought up in Plymouth Sound.
She hears the gun. My husband's come, to him I must go down.
She goes unto her neighbour's house. One thing of you I crave
Lend me your gown for mine's in pawn, it's the only one I have.

Then she goes down unto the Sound and tries for to get in
She so loudly for her husband calls and runs and kisses him
Saying, How happy we shall be, my dear, now you are safe on shore
You shall sit at home with me, my love, and go to sea no more.

Don't Let Me Die an Old Maid

Hammond D362. William Miller, Wootton Fitzpaine, Dorset. April 1906.

Come all you young fellows, just give your attention
There's something partic'lar that I've got to mention.
You're living quite near me in numbers a-plenty
Will one of you court me? I'm just five-and-twenty.

Chorus: *To my right fol the diddle, right fol the diddle*
          Whack fol the diddle li do.

My mother and father say I'm in the lurch now
Then surely 'tis time someone took me to church now.
Some fourteen, some fifteen, some sixteen when they marry
I'm five-and-twenty, I must no longer tarry.

There's my sister Susan, she's crooked and misshapen
Before she was sixteen a bride she was taken.
Before she was eighteen she'd a son and a daughter
At my five-and-twenty, I've ne'er had an offer.

There's my sister Sarah, she's younger than I am
She's got nine or ten sweethearts and still she denies 'em.
I wish I had one, I don't want so many
And I've not been guilty of denying of any.

There's my sister Caroline, she's plain and she's simple
And near to her left eye there grows a large pimple.
She's got a young man not quite right in the head
And they sit up a-courting after we go to bed.

32

Then there's Widow Toss-Pot at the sign of the Cutler
She's setting her cap to catch Squire Smith's butler.
She's buried three husbands and thinks it quite fun
While I'm five-and-twenty and cannot catch one.

I've often been told, 'tis by my old mother
Going to a wedding soon brings on another.
Now if I thought so I'd go without bidding
So judge me, young men, if I don't want wedding.

I'd make a good wife, not scolding or jealous
I'd find him with money to spend at the alehouse.
While he was 'broad spending, I'd be at home mending
So judge me, young men, if that isn't commending.

Come shoemaker, blacksmith, come tinker, come tailor
Come fifer, come drummer, come soldier, come sailor
Come old or come young, come foolish or witty
Don't let me did an old maid, but take me for pity.

THE EVERLASTING CIRCLE

Gardiner C13. William Lugg, Launceston, Cornwall. February 1905.

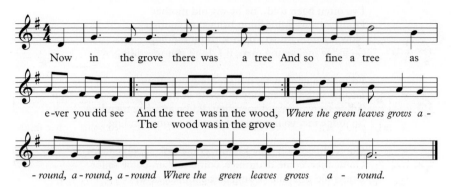

Now in the grove there was a tree
And so fine a tree as ever you did see
And the tree was in the wood, the wood was in the grove
> *Where the green leaves grows around, around, around*
> *Where the green leaves grows around.*

Now in this tree there came a limb
And so fine a limb as ever you did see
And the limb was in the tree, the tree was in the wood, etc.

Now in this limb there came a branch
And so fine a branch, etc.

Now in this branch there came a nest
And so fine a nest, etc.

Now in this nest there came an egg
And so fine an egg, etc.

Now in this egg there came a bird
And so fine a bird, etc.

Now of this bird there came a feather
And so fine a feather, etc.

Now of this feather there came a bed
And so fine a bed, etc.

Now of this bed there came a maid
And so fine a maid, etc.

Now of this maid there came a man
And so fine a man, etc.

Now by this man was planted a seed
And so fine a seed, etc.

Now of this seed there came a tree,
And so fine a tree, etc.

A Fair Maid Walking in Her Garden

Text: Hammond D393. John Pomery, Bridport Union, Dorset. May 1906.
Tune: Hammond D566. Mrs Steer, South Perrot, Dorset. July 1906.

A fair maid walk - ing all in__ her gar - den
A brisk young sail - or she chanced to spy. He step-ped up to her think-
-ing__ to gain__ her And said, Fair maid, can you fan - cy I?

A fair maid walking all in her garden
A brisk young sailor she chanced to spy.
He stepped up to her thinking to gain her
And said, Fair maid, can you fancy I?

You seem to me like some man of honour
A man of honour you seem to be.
How can you impose on a poor young
       woman
Who is not fit your servant to be?

Well, if you are not fit to be my servant
Yet I have a great regard for thee.
I'll marry you, I'll make you my lady
And you'll have servants to wait on thee.

But I have a true lover of my own, sir
And seven years he's been gone from me
And seven years more I will wait all for him
For if he's alive he will be true to me.

If for seven long years your love have left you
I'm sure he's either dead or drowned.
Well, and if he's alive I do love him dearly
And if he's dead I hope he's in glory crowned.

When he saw that his true love was loyal
Down before her he did fall
Saying, I am that poor and young single
       sailor
Which many long years on the ocean sail.

If you are my poor and young single sailor
Show me the token I gave to thee
For seven long years have made an alteration
Since my true-love have gone to sea.

He pulled his hands out of his bosom
His fingers being both long and small.
Here is the ring that was broke between us.
And when she saw it then down she fall.

He took her up all in his arms
Giving her kisses one, two and three
Saying, I am your poor and young single sailor
Just now returned for to marry thee.

FAIR SUSAN I LEFT

Tune: Hammond D407. John Pomery, Bridport Union, Dorset. May 1906.
Tune: Hammond D477. R Larcombe, Beaminster Workhouse, Dorset. June 1906.

Fair Su - san_ I left_ with my heart_ full of woe And_ to
sea went my for - tunes to mend While her soft swell - ing bo - som heaved
ma - ny_ a sigh As she part - ed from her true_ lov - ing_ friend.

ⴲ *Suggested alternative ending*

friend As she part - ed from her true_ lov - ing_ friend.

Fair Susan I left with my heart full of woe
And to sea went my fortunes to mend
While her soft swelling bosom heaved many a sigh
As she parted from her true loving friend.

Farewell, Jack! she cried, as she bid him adieu
While the tears from her eyes they did flow
And away I did go with my heart full of woe
For to join with some jovial ship's crew.

The wind did blow hard and the seas did run high
And the thunder all round us did roar
And I thought of my Susan that I leaved behind
And I thought not to see her no more.

Our ship sprung a leak and all hands called on deck
Every man his own life for to save
I swum on a plank and got safe from the wreck
But the rest met a watery grave.

And since that good fortune had saved my life
I thought to my Susan I'd go
I thought for to make her my own lawful wife
But my pleasure all turned into woe.

When the news reached her ears that our gallant ship was lost
And that Jack would be hers no more
She died like a rose that's been nipped by the frost
And left me her loss to deplore.

THE FEMALE CABIN BOY

Gardiner H1148. William Hill, Catherington Workhouse, Hampshire. August 1908.

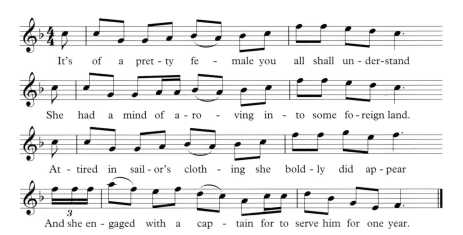

It's of a pretty fe - male you all shall un - der-stand
She had a mind of a - ro - ving in - to some fo - reign land.
At - tired in sail - or's cloth - ing she bold - ly did ap - pear
And she en - gaged with a cap - tain for to serve him for one year.

It's of a pretty female you all shall understand
She had a mind of a-roving into some foreign land.
Attired in sailor's clothing she boldly did appear
And she engaged with a captain to serve him for one year.

She engaged with a captain a cabin boy to be
The wind it was in favour so they soon put out to sea.
The captain's lady being on board she seemed in great joy
So glad the captain had engaged such a handsome cabin boy.

So nimble was this pretty maid and done her duty well
But mark what followed after, and song itself will tell
The captain with this pretty maid did often sport and toy
For he soon found out the secret of the pretty cabin boy.

Her cheeks appeared like roses and with her sidelocks curled
The sailors often smiled and said he looked just like a girl.
By eating captain's biscuit her colour did destroy
And the waist did swell of pretty Nell, the handsome cabin boy.

It was through the Bay of Biscay our gallant ship did plough
One night amongst the sailors there was a pretty row.
They bundled from their hammocks, it did their rest destroy
And it was all about the groanings of the handsome cabin boy.

O doctor, o doctor! the cabin boy did cry.
The sailors swore by all that's good the cabin boy would die.
The doctor run with all his might a-smiling at the fun
For to think that a sailor lad should have a daughter or a son.

The sailors when they heard the joke they all began to stare
The child belonged to none of them they solemnly did swear.
The lady to the captain said, My dear, I wish you joy
For 'twas either you or I betrayed the handsome cabin boy.

THE FARMERS' TOAST

Gardiner H912. Frank Gamblin, Portsmouth Workhouse, Hampshire. August 1907.

Come all jolly fellows that love to be mellow
Attend unto me and sit easy.
My glass is now dry, so to sing I will try
For dull thinking will make a man crazy.
For here I am king, let us drink, laugh and sing
Let no man appear as a stranger
For the jingling of glasses all music surpasses
And I likes to see bottles a-draining.
> *Fal le ral le ral lal, fal le ral le ral lee*
> *And I likes to see bottles a-draining.*

Let the wealthy and great roll in splendour and state
I envy them not I declare it.
I'll eat my own lamb, my own chicken and ham
I'll shear my own sheep and I'll wear it.
Was it not for my seeding you'd get but poor feeding
I am sure you would all starve without me
I am always content when I've paid my rent
And happy when friends are about me.
>   *Fal-le-ral-le-ral-lal, fal-le-ral-le-ral-lee*
>   *And happy when friends are about me.*

To the second part of the tune:

I have lawns, I have bowers, I have fruit, I have flowers
The lark is my daily alarmer
So my jolly boys now that follows the plough
Drink health and success to the farmer.
>   *Fal le ral le ral lal, fal le ral le ral lee*
>   *Drink health and success to the farmer.*

THE FRIAR IN THE WELL

Hammond D629. Mr J Penny, Poole, Dorset. October 1906.
Hammond D661. Mr F Stockley, Wareham, Dorset. November 1906.

It's of an old friar as I have been told *Fal the dal did-dle i dee*____

He court-ed a young maid just six-teen years old *Fal the dal did-dle i dee.*____

He came to the maid as she lay on her bed And swore he would have her maid-en-head

To my fe - ro le - ro lid - dle____ Sing twice to my lank-y down der - ry, o!

It's of an old friar as I have been told
Fal the dal diddle i dee
He courted a young maid just sixteen
years old
Fal the dal diddle i dee.
He came to the maid as she lay on
her bed
And swore he would have her
maidenhead
To my fero lero liddle
*Sing twice to my lanky down
derry, o!*

Oh no, said the maid, for you know
very well
If we do such things we should go to hell.
No matter, my dear, you need have
no doubt
If you was in hell I could sing you out.

Oh then, said the maid, you shall have
this thing
But you to me ten shillings must bring.
And while he went home the money
to fetch
She thought to herself how the old friar
she could catch.

Now while he was gone, the truth to tell
She hung a cloth in front of the well.
He knocked at the door, the maid let
him in.
Oh now, my dear, oh let us begin.

Then Alas, cried the maid, all crafty and
cunning
I think I hear my father a-coming.
So behind the cloth the old friar did trip
And into the well he happened to slip.

The friar called out with a pitiful sound
Oh help me out or I shall be drowned.
You said you could sing my soul out of hell
Well, now you can sing yourself out of
the well.

So she helped him out and bid him be gone
And the friar he wanted his money again.
Oh no, said the maid, I'll have none of
the matter
For indeed you must pay me for
dirtying the water.

So out of the house the old friar did creep
Dripping his arse like a newly-dipped sheep
And young and old commended the maid
For the very pretty trick she had played.

THE FURZE FIELD

Gardiner H737. Moses Mills, Preston Candover, Alresford, Hampshire. July 1907.

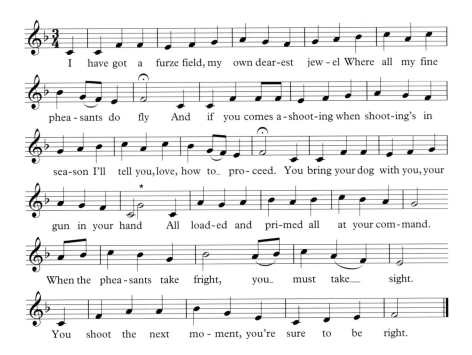

I have got a furze field, my own dearest jewel
Where all my fine pheasants do fly
And if you comes a-shooting when shooting's in season
I'll tell you, love, how to proceed.
You bring your dog with you, your gun in your hand
All loaded and primed all at your command.
When the pheasants take fright, you must take sight.
You shoot the next moment, you're sure to be right.

I have got a fishpond, my own dearest jewel
Where all my fine fishes do play
And if you comes a-fishing when fishing's in season
I'll tell you, love, how to proceed.
You bring your nets with you, your rod in your hand
Your hooks and your angles all at your command.
When you throws in, all the fishes will play
It's down to the bottom and that's the right way.

I have got a warren, my own dearest jewel
Where all my fine rabbits do play
And if you comes a-ferreting when ferreting's in season
I'll tell you, love, how to proceed.
You bring your dog with you, your ferret in your hand
Your spade and your nets all at your command
And the ferret will bolt and the rabbits will play
For it's down to the bottom and that's the right way.

I have got a park, my own dearest jewel
Where all my fine deers I do keep
And if you comes a-hunting when hunting's in season
I'll tell you, love, how to proceed.
You bring your dog with you, your nag in your hand
All saddled and bridled, all at your command
And the deers they will prowl and the dogs they will brawl
And it's then, Gee up, Dobbin! and back they will fall.

To the second half of the tune:

Oh some do like hunting and some do like game
And shooting a pheasant is gentlemen's game
But fishing in a fishpond is all my delight
Go down to the bottom, you're sure to be right.

THE GAME OF ALL FOURS

Tune: Gardiner H73. William Randall, Hursley, Hampshire. June 1905.
Text: Gardiner H1142. Fred Osman, Lower Bartley, Hampshire. November 1908.

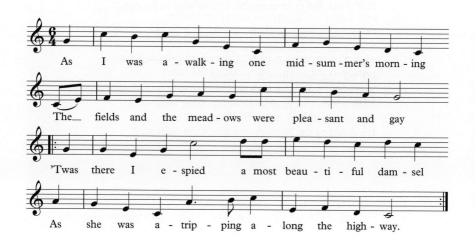

As I was a-walk-ing one mid-sum-mer's morn-ing
The— fields and the mead-ows were plea-sant and gay
'Twas there I e-spied a most beau-ti-ful dam-sel
As she was a-trip-ping a-long the high-way.

As I was a-walking one midsummer's morning
The fields and the meadows were pleasant and gay
'Twas there I espied a most beautiful damsel
As she was a-tripping along the highway.
'Twas there I espied a most beautiful damsel
As she was a-tripping along the highway.

I stepped up to her and wished her good morning
And where are you going so soon in the morn?
She answered, Kind sir, I'm a-going to Windsor
To that pleasant place where I was born.
She answered, etc.

I says, Fair maid, and shall I go with you
All for to bear you sweet company?
She turned herself round and smiling so sweetly
Kind sir, you may do just as you please.
She turned herself round, etc.

We had not been walking past a mile together
Before that we better acquainted became.
I says, Fair girl, come sit you down by me
And I will show you a sweet, pleasant game.
I says, Fair girl, etc.

She says, Kind sir, I'm not given to gaming
But nevertheless I'm willing to learn
But the game that we play it must be All Fours
And then I will hold you three to one.
But the game that we play, etc.

She cut the cards and 'twas my turn to deal them
I dealt myself one trump, 'twas only poor jack
And she had the ace and the deuce for to beat me
And they are the very best cards in the pack.
And she had the ace, etc.

She played off her ace and she took the jack from me
Which made her high, low, jack and the game.
She says, Kind sir, I've fairly a-beat you
Or else we will play the game over again.
She says, Kind sir, etc.

I picked up my hat and I wished her good morning
And left her high, low, jack and the game.
I says, Fair girl, I'll be this way tomorrow
And then we will play the game over again.
I says, Fair girl, etc.

GAMEKEEPERS LIE SLEEPING

Tune: Gardiner H680. Charles Bull (senior), Marchwood, Southampton. June 1907.

Text: Gardiner H1142. James Ray (junior), Petersfield, Hampshire. August 1908.

Note: This time signature is only approximate. The song should be sung freely, and any accompaniment should be non-rhythmic.

I got a dog and a good dog too I keeps him in my keep-ing

For to catch those hares that run by night Whilst the game-keep-ers lie sleep-ing.

I got a dog and a good dog too
I keeps him in my keeping
For to catch those hares that run by night
Whilst the gamekeepers lie sleeping.

My dogs and me went out one night
For to learn some education.
Up jumps a hare and away she run
Right into a large plantation.

She had not gone so very far
Before something stopped her running.
O aunt, o aunt! she loudly cried
Stop a minute, your uncle's coming.

Then I took out my old penknife
And quickly I did paunch her.
She turned out one of the female kind
How glad am I, I caught her.

I picks her up and I smooth her down
And I puts her in my keeping.
I says to my dog, It's time to be going
Whilst the gamekeepers are still sleeping.

Away me and my dog did go
Back into the town.
I takes this hare to a labouring man
And I sells her for a crown.

We called into some public house
And there we got quite merry (mellow)
For we spent that crown and another one too
Don't you think I'm a good-hearted fellow?

GOSSIP JOAN

Hammond D657. Joseph Vincent, Wareham, Dorset. November 1906.

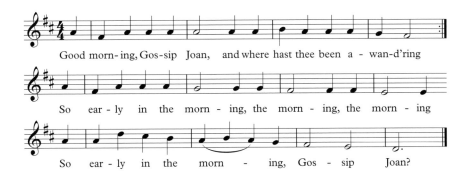

Good morn-ing, Gos-sip Joan, and where hast thee been a-wan-d'ring
So ear-ly in the morn - ing, the morn - ing, the morn - ing
So ear-ly in the morn - ing, Gos - sip Joan?

Good morning, Gossip Joan, and where hast thee been a-wand'ring
Good morning, Gossip Joan, and where hast thee been a-wand'ring
So early in the morning, the morning, the morning
So early in the morning, Gossip Joan?

Our dog's gone to the copse and I can't tell where to find him
Our dog's gone to the copse and I can't tell where to find him.
Leave him alone, he'll soon come home, he'll soon come home,
        he'll soon come home
And bring his tail behind him, Gossip Joan.

I have an idle girl and she will not rock the cradle
I have an idle girl and she will not rock the cradle.
To beat her I'm afraid, I'm afraid, I'm afraid
Because I am not able, Gossip Joan.

Our pig he is not well. Pray tell me what's the matter
Our pig he is not well. Pray tell me what's the matter.
'Twas but the other day, the other day, the other day
He ate the wooden platter, Gossip Joan.

Our duck she swallowed a snail and by zooks, ain't that a wonder
Our duck she swallowed a snail and by zooks, ain't that a wonder.
For the horns grew out of her tail, her tail, her tail
And split her rump asunder, Gossip Joan.

Our cow she had a calf underneath the parlour window
Our cow she had a calf underneath the parlour window.
And if it hadn't been for the bull's hulloa, hulloa, hulloa
She wouldn't have had her labour, Gossip Joan.

Let's to the alehouse go and wash down all our sorrows
Let's to the alehouse go and wash down all our sorrows.
I'll tell you all my troubles, my troubles, my troubles
And we'll meet again tomorrow, Gossip Joan.★

★or: For we may not meet tomorrow, Gossip Joan.

Green Bushes

Tune: Hammond D559. Ishmael Cornick, Burstock, Dorset. June 1906.
Text: Hammond D202. George Dowden, Piddlehinton, Dorset. June 1905.

As I was a-walking one morning in the spring
For to hear the birds a-whistle and the nightingales sing
Oh I heard a fair damsel, so sweetaly sang she
Down by the green bushes where she chanced to meet me.

I stepped up to this fair maid and unto her did say
How far are you a-going for to wander this way?
I'm a-waiting for my true-love, kind sir, then said she
Down by these green bushes where he vowed to meet me.

I'll buy you a fine beaver and a fine silken gown
I'll buy you fine petticoats all flounced to the ground
If you will prove loyal and constant to me
And forsake your own true-love and get married to me.

I'll have none of your beaver nor your fine silken hose
For I never was so poor as to marry for clothes
But if you will prove loyal and constant to me
I'll forsake my own true-love and get married to thee.

Come let us be going, kind sir, if you please
Come let us now be going all from under these trees
For yonder is a-coming my true-love I see
Down by the green bushes where he thinks to meet me.

And when he came there and he found she was gone
He stood like some lambkin that was all forlorn.
She has gone with some other and quite forsaken me
So adieu to green bushes for ever, said he.

Now I'll be like some schoolboy and spend my time in play
For I never was so foolish to be deluded away.
There is never a false woman shall serve me so no more
So adieu to green bushes, it's time to give o'er.

THE GREY HAWK

Hammond D269. Robert Barratt, Piddletown, Dorset. September/October 1905.

Once I had a grey hawk and a pretty grey hawk A___ sweet pretty bird of my own___ But she took a flight, she flew a-way quite And there's no - bo - dy knows where she's gone, my brave boys And there's no - bo - dy knows where she's gone.___

Once I had a grey hawk and a pretty grey hawk
A sweet pretty bird of my own
But she took a flight, she flew away quite
And there's nobody knows where she's gone, my brave boys
And there's nobody knows where she's gone.

It's over the wide forest I rambled away
And through the green fields I did stray
I holloa'd, I whooped, I played on my flute
Not my sweet pretty bird could I find, my brave boys
Not my sweet pretty bird could I find.

Then it's over the green hills I rambled away
And through the green paths I did stray
Oh there I did spy my sweet pretty bird
She was close by the side of a man, my brave boys
She was close by the side of a man.

Now he that has got her is welcome to keep her
And do the best with her he can
But whiles he have her and I have her not
I will hawk with her once now and then, my brave boys
I will hawk with her once now and then.

How happy's the man that has a good wife
Much better is he that's got none
But cursèd is he that courteth another's
When he has a good wife of his own, my brave boys
When he has a good wife of his own.

47

THE GREY MARE

Gardiner H391. Alfred Oliver, Axford, Basingstoke, Hampshire. September 1907.

Young Roger the miller he courted of late
A farmer's fair daughter called beautiful Kate
And she to her portion had jewels and rings
And she to her portion, and she to her portion had many fine things.

Oh the marriage was ordered, the money paid down
It was a fine fortune, full five thousand pounds.
This glittering money and jewels beside
Quite tickled his fancy, quite tickled his fancy and dazzled his eyes.

The day of the wedding came lovely and fair
Her father rode up on a beautiful mare
Which causèd young Roger to vow and declare
He would not have the daughter, he would not have the daughter without the grey mare.

Then the old man replied to Roger with speed
I thought you would marry my daughter indeed
But since it is so I am never the worse
My money once more, my money once more I will put in my purse.

Then the money soon vanished right out of his sight
And so did Miss Kate his joy and delight
Then Roger he tore the locks of his hair
And he wished he had never, and he wished he had never stood for the grey mare.

A year or two after a little above
By chance then he met with Miss Kitty his love.
A-smiling says Roger, Why, don't you know me?
If I'm not mistaken, if I'm not mistaken, I've seen you, said she.

A man much your likeness with long yellow hair
He once came a-courting my father's grey mare.
Now fare thee well, Roger, get out of my sight
Now fare thee well, Roger, now fare thee well, Roger, I wish you goodnight.

Oh no, then said Roger, you are much to blame
It was unto you a-courting I came
But since your father has lost such a beautiful son
I am now very sorry, I am now very sorry for what I have done.

THE GRUMBLING FARMERS

Gardiner C19. Mr J Boaden, Cury Cross Lanes, Helston, Cornwall. May 1905.

Farmers Marco and Pedro were jogging along
They had both been to market together.
They grumbled that this thing and that thing was wrong
And they grumbled about the dry weather.
They talked of the wars and of things old and new
And they talked of the saints and their sins (not a few!)
And they prayed to their saints for a shower or two
As a-grumbling they jogged along together.

Chorus: *Singing yaddle faddle fiddle faddle, right fal laddle lay*
And my yaddle faddle tiddle taddle, right fal laddle lay
And they prayed to their saints for a shower or two
As a-grumbling they jogged along together.

The saints heard their prayers for the sky 'gan to cloud
They were both of them put to their tether.
The rain he poured down and the thunders roared loud
And they wished themselves home both together.
At length to the church by good luck they drew nigh
And into the church porch together they did hie
And they talked of the dead that around them did lie
Regardless of wind and of weather.

Chorus: *Singing yaddle faddle fiddle faddle, etc.*
          And they talked of the dead that around them did lie
          Regardless of wind and of weather.

Says Marco, This rain will be gloriously found
And my heart is as light as a feather.
It will shortly bring all things up out of the ground
And everything will spring up together.
God forbid, said old Pedro, that would be my lot
Three wives in this churchyard buried I've got
If it rains cats and dogs I must promptly leave this spot
And he toddled off in spite of the weather.

Chorus: *Singing yaddle faddle fiddle faddle, etc.*
          If it rains cats and dogs I must promptly leave this spot
          And he toddled off in spite of the weather.

HOME, DEAREST HOME

Hammond D514. William Chubb, Beaminster, Dorset. June 1906.

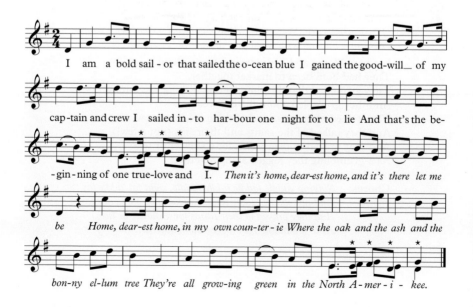

I am a bold sail-or that sailed the o-cean blue I gained the good-will_ of my
cap-tain and crew I sailed in-to har-bour one night for to lie And that's the be-
-gin-ning of one true-love and I. *Then it's home, dear-est home, and it's there let me*
be Home, dear-est home, in my own coun-ter-ie Where the oak and the ash and the
bon-ny el-lum tree They're all grow-ing green in the North A-mer-i-kee.

I am a bold sailor that sailed the ocean blue
I gained the goodwill of my captain and crew
I sailed into harbour one night for to lie
And that's the beginning of one* true-love and I.

Chorus: *Then it's home, dearest home, and it's there let me be
            Home, dearest home, in my own counterie
            Where the oak and the ash and the bonny ellum tree
            They're all growing green in the North Amerikee.*

He asked for a candle to light him to bed
Likewise for a napkin to tie round his head.
She waited on me as a fair maid should do
And I gave her the wink to jump into bed too.

She jumped into bed for to keep herself warm
Not thinking a sailor would do her any harm.
She kissed him, she cuddled him, she bid him draw near
She wished that long night had been seven long year.

And early in the morning this sailor he arose
And out of his pocket brought silver and gold
Saying, Take this, oh take this, for the mischief I have done
For this night I leave to you a daughter or a son.

Now, when the baby's born you shall put it out to nurse
With silver in its pocket and gold in its purse.
You shall dry up your milk as a virgin so free
And pass for a maid in some strange counterie.

And if it be a girl you shall dangle it on your knee
But if it be a boy you shall send him off to sea
With his tarry blue jumper and his jacket of navy blue
He'll go climbing up the riggings like his daddy used to do.

Come all you fair maidens, a warning take by me
And never trust a sailor one inch above your knee
For I have trusted one and he has deceived me
And he's left me with a baby to dangle on my knee.

Mr Chubb sang 'my'.

I LIVE NOT WHERE I LOVE

Hammond D219. Robert Barratt, Piddletown, Dorset. September/October 1905.

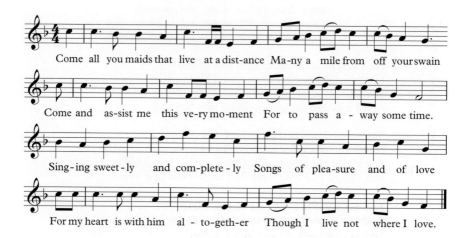

Come all you maids that live at a dist-ance Ma-ny a mile from off your swain
Come and as-sist me this ve-ry mo-ment For to pass a - way some time.
Sing-ing sweet-ly and com-plete-ly Songs of plea-sure and of love
For my heart is with him al - to-geth-er Though I live not where I love.

Come all you maids that live at a
distance
Many a mile from off your swain
Come and assist me this very moment
For to pass away some time.
Singing sweetly and completely
Songs of pleasure and of love
For my heart is with him altogether
Though I live not where I love.

When I sleep I dream about you
When I wake I take no rest
For every instant thinking on you
My heart e'er fixèd in your breast
And although far distance may be
        assistance
From my mind his love to remove
But my heart is with him altogether
Though I live not where I love.

All the world shall be of one religion
All living things shall cease to die
Before I prove false unto my jewel
Or any way my love deny.
The world shall change and be most
        strange
If ever I my mind remove
My heart is with him altogether
Though I live not where I love.

So farewell lads and farewell lasses
Now I think I've got my choice.
I will away to yonder mountains
Where I think I hear his voice.
And if he holloa I will follow
Around the world though 'tis
        so wide
For young Thomas he did promise
I should be his lawful bride.

THE INDIAN LASS

Tune: Hammond D386. Mrs Forsey, Watton, Dorset. May 1906.
Text: Hammond D355. Captain Love, Lyme Regis, Dorset. April 1906.

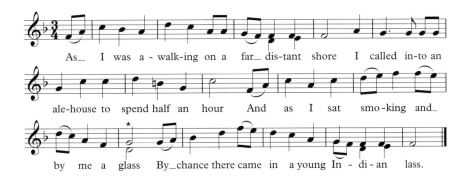

As__ I was a-walk-ing on a far__ dis-tant shore I called in-to an ale-house to spend half an hour And as I sat smo-king and__ by me a glass By__chance there came in a young In - di-an lass.

As I was a-walking on a far distant shore
I called into an alehouse to spend half an hour
And as I sat smoking and by me a glass
By chance there came in a young Indian lass.

I viewed this young Indian in the place where she stood
I viewed her fair features and found they were good.
She was neat, tall and handsome, and her age was sixteen
She was born and brought up in a place called New Orleans.

She sat down beside me and squeezed my hand
Kind sir, you are a stranger, not one of this land
And if you have not lodgings with me you shall stay
And dearly I'll love you by night and by day.

We tossed and we tumbled in each other's arms
And all that long night I enjoyed her sweet charms
And as I embraced her, oh this was her tone
You are a poor sailor and far from your home.

With mutual enjoyment the time passed away
Till the day was appointed for us to sail away.
She said, When that you are on your own native land
Remember the young Indian that squeezed your hand.

The hour was appointed that we were to sail
This lovely young Indian on the beach did bewail.
I took out my handkerchief and wipèd her eyes
Oh do not go and leave me, dear sailor, she cried.

We weighèd our anchor and away then we flew
A sweet pleasant gale parted her from my view
And now that I'm over and taking my glass
I'll drink a good health to the Indian lass.

The Innkeeper's Daughter

Hammond D686. Mr J Bridle, Stratton, Dorset. November/December 1906.

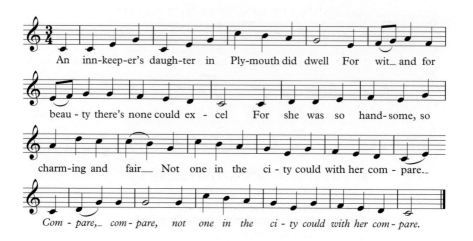

An inn-keep-er's daugh-ter in Ply-mouth did dwell For wit_ and for beau - ty there's none could ex - cel For she was so hand-some, so charm-ing and fair_ Not one in the ci - ty could with her com - pare._ Com - pare,_ com - pare, not one in the ci - ty could with her com - pare.

An innkeeper's daughter in Plymouth did dwell
For wit and for beauty there's none could excel
For she was so handsome, so charming and fair
Not one in the city could with her compare.
        Compare, compare, not one in the city could with her compare.

She was courted by a sailor and John was his name
And to this Jack Tar she engaged became
But as they appointed for their wedding day
He received his orders for to sail away.
        Sail away, sail away, he received his orders for to sail away.

He said, Then, my dear, since it must be so
Seven years' long voyage to the Indies I must go
And when I return I'll marry you, my dear
And then we will live in great splendour, don't fear.
        Don't fear, don't fear, etc.

Before seven long years were over and past
A bold tailor of Plymouth his love did embrace
And all things being ready for their wedding day
When home comes the sailor as I have heard say.
        Heard say, heard say, etc.

As he was a-walking up through Plymouth Street
He chanced for to meet with a brother shipmate.
Oh don't you remember your once courting a maid?
She is going to be married as I have heard said.
        Heard said, heard said, etc.

He shook his head and he gave such a smile.
How do they know but their sport might be spoiled?
He went and bought licence that very same night
And back to his true-love just as 'twas daylight.
Daylight, daylight, etc.

And when he came there he took her by the hand
You are going to be married as I understand
So now I am come for to know your design
For you are my true-love and you shall be mine.
Be mine, be mine, etc.

Oh, then said the fair one, and what shall I do?
I know very well I am promised to you.
Since you are my true-love I shall be your bride
And no man in this world will I marry beside.
Beside, beside, etc.

So this was appointed, 'twas their wedding day.
Poor tailor was chosen to give the bride away.
Poor tailor not knowing how his passion to rule
Went up like a man and came back like a fool.
A fool, a fool, etc.

So come all you bold tailors wherever you dwell
If you've a mind for to marry, marry when you will.
If you've a mind to marry, oh make no delay
For fear that Jack Tar shall steal her away.
Away, away, etc.

JOHN APPLEBY

Hammond D359. William Miller, Wootton Fitzpaine, Dorset. April 1906.

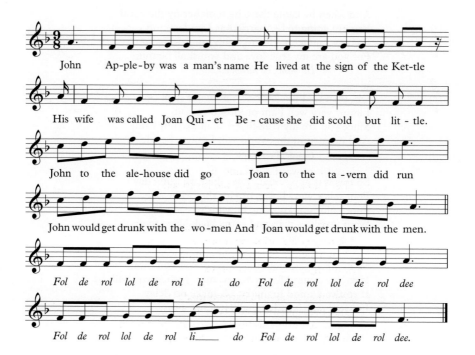

John Appleby was a man's name
He lived at the sign of the Kettle
His wife was called Joan Quiet
Because she did scold but little.
John to the alehouse did go
Joan to the tavern did run
John would get drunk with the women
And Joan would get drunk with the men.

Chorus: *Fol de rol lol de rol li do*
            Fol de rol lol de rol dee
            Fol de rol lol de rol li do
            Fol de rol lol de rol dee.

John was no great eater
Joan she was no glutton
For to tickle their jaws
She bought a shoulder of mutton.
John being in an angry mood
Took the mutton in hand
And out of the window he flung it
While Joan was put at a stand.

Joan was standing by
She thought it didn't matter.
She never said a word
But after it throwed the platter.
A woman coming by
Seeing the mutton lay
Took up the mutton and platter
And with it runned away.

Neighbours coming in
Thinking to end the quarrel
Good Lord! When they had done
There wasn't a drop in the barrel.
They banged the barrel about
Pulled out the spicket too
We'll all get drunk tonight
For there's nothing else to do.

JOHN BLUNT

Hammond D715. Mrs Seale, Dorchester Union, Dorset. December 1906.

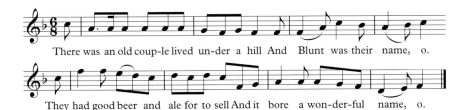

There was an old coup-le lived un-der a hill And Blunt was their name, o.

They had good beer and ale for to sell And it bore a won-der-ful name, o.

There was an old couple lived under a hill
And Blunt was their name, o.
They had good beer and ale for to sell
And it bore a wonderful name, o.

John Blunt and his wife drank free of this ale
Till they could drink no more, o.
Then it's off to bed this old couple went
And forgot to bar the door, o.

Then they a bargain, bargain made
They made it strong and sure, o
The which of them should speak the first word
Should go down and bar the door, o.

Then there came travellers, travellers three
Travelling in the night, o.
No house, nor home, nor fire had they
Nor yet no candlelight, o.

Then straight to John Blunt's house they went
And gently opened the door, o.
The devil a word the old couple spoke
For fear which should bar the door, o.

They went to his cellar and drank up his drink
Till they could drink no more, o.
They went to his cupboard and ate up his meat
Till they could eat no more, o.

Then quickly they procured a light
And gently walked upstairs, o.
They pulled the old woman out of her bed
And put her on the floor, o.

Up speaks John Blunt, You've ate of my meat
And laid my wife on the floor, o.
You've spoke the first word, John Blunt, she said
Go down and bar the door, o!

King William and the Keeper

Hammond D99. George Roper (of Charlton St Mary) in Blandford Union, Dorset.
August (?) 1905.

You subjects of England I pray you draw near
A comical story you quickly shall hear
'Tis concerning King William and his keeper also
That met in the forest some winters ago.

King William rose early all on a May morn
And a-hunting he went in a forest his own.
'Twas a suit of brown russet King William put on
As though he had been some silly poor man.

Then up spoke young Mary our most precious queen
King William, King William, oh where art thou going?
Oh it must be a fool or some very unwise man
That would tell of his counsel unto a woman.

The queen in her modest behaviour replied
May Providence be with thee and still be thy guide
To keep you from danger, my sovereign lord
Which will the greatest of blessings afford.

Then away to the forest King William did ride
Where his greyhounds ran swift and the keeper drew nigh
Saying, Begone, thou proud fellow, thou shalt have no sport here
Without the consent of King William, forbear.

I'm one of his subjects, not one of his foes
I've only come here to run one course or two.
Get you gone, you bold fellow, you'll run no course here
Without leave of King William to hunt the fat deer.

Says the king, I've two horses I'll freely give thee
Besides my two greyhounds so good as they be
Besides I will give you full forty shillings
If thou'll not betray me to William our king.

I'll not have thy horses thou'st offered to me
I'll not have thy greyhounds so good as they be
But I'll have thee before him as sure as a gun
And there thou shalt answer for what thou hast done.

The king in his modest behaviour replied
Oh dost thou not see the bright star on my side?
The forest is mine, I'd have thee to know
Then pray why's the reason thou'st threaten me so?

At this the bold keeper fell all on his knees.
Your Majesty's pardon, do just as you please.
The blood in my body begins to run cold
Your Majesty's pardon for being so bold.

Arise, my bold keeper, and shake off thy fear
For by me no harm shalt thou ever come near.
For if all of my subjects were loyal as thee
Oh what a brave man King William would be.

Because I'd encourage such fellows as you
I'll make thee my ranger, and if that will not do
Thou shalt be a captain, by land or by sea
And for evermore in my favour shall be.

The keeper replied, My sovereign lord
Sure I am not worthy of such a reward.
Yet nevertheless your true keeper I'll be
Because I'm afraid for to venture at sea.

At this the king laughed till his sides he did hold
And threw him down fifty bright guineas in gold
And bid him make haste to Kensington Court
Where he of this jest would make of much sport.

And when you get there enquire for Long Jack
He wears a drum major's coat on his back
Likewise a white pheasant marked on his right sleeve
And he is a true man, you may him believe.

He's one of my porters who stands at the gate
To let in my nobles both early and late
And therefore, good fellow, come up without fear.
I'll make thee my ranger of parks far and near.

JUST AS THE TIDE WAS FLOWING

Hammond D570. Walter Diment, Cheddington, Dorset. July 1906.

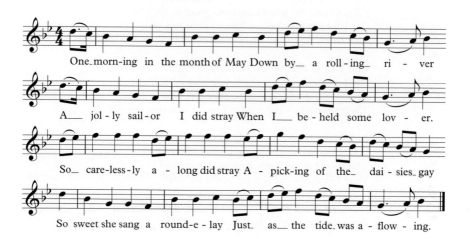

One morn-ing in the month of May Down by a roll-ing ri-ver
A jol-ly sail-or I did stray When I be-held some lov-er.
So care-less-ly a-long did stray A-pick-ing of the dai-sies gay
So sweet she sang a round-e-lay Just as the tide was a-flow-ing.

One morning in the month of May
Down by a rolling river
A jolly sailor I did stray
When I beheld some lover.
So carelessly along did stray
A-picking of the daisies gay
So sweet she sang a roundelay
Just as the tide was a-flowing.

Oh her dress it was as white as milk
And her jewels did adorn her
Her shoes were made of the
    crimson silk
Just like some lady of honour.
Her cheeks were red, her eyes
    were brown
Her hair in ringlets hanging down
She'd a lovely brow without a frown
Just as the tide was a-flowing.

I made a bow and said, Fair maid
How come you here so early?
My heart by you it is betrayed
For I could love you dearly.
I am a sailor come from sea
If you will accept of my company
To walk and view the fishes play
Just as the tide is a-flowing.

No more we said, but on the way
We ganged along together.
The small birds sang and the lambs
    did play
And pleasant was the weather.
When we were weary we both sat down
Beneath a tree with the branches around
And what was done shall never be found
As long as the tide is a-flowing.

But as she lay upon the grass
Her colours they kept changing
Till she cried out and said, Alas!
Never let your mind be ranging.
Here is twenty pounds I have in store
Meet me when you will, there's plenty more
For my jolly sailor I adore
Just as the tide is a-flowing.

We both shook hands and off we steer
Jack Tar drinks rum and brandy.
To keep his shipmates in good cheer
The lady's gold is handy.
And along with some other pretty maid I
    will go
To a public house where the brandy do flow
Success to the maid that will do so
Just as the tide is a-flowing.

THE LARK IN THE MORNING

Hammond D102. George Roper (of Charlton St Mary), Blandford Union, Dorset. 1905.

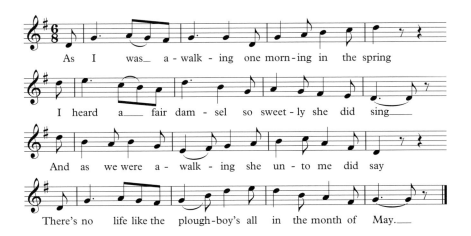

As I was a-walking one morning in the spring
I heard a fair damsel so sweetly she did sing
And as we were a-walking she unto me did say
There's no life like the ploughboy's all in the month of May.

The lark in the morning she rises from her nest
And mounts in the bright air with the dew all on her breast
And with the pretty ploughboy she'll whistle and she'll sing
And at night she'll return to her nest back again.

When the ploughboy has done all that he has to do
Perhaps to the country wake a-walking he will go
And there with his lassie he'll dance and he'll sing
And at night they'll return to their homes back again.

And as they return from the wake of the town
The meadows being mown and the grass all cut down
If they should chance to tumble all on the new mown hay
It's, Kiss me now or never, this pretty maid would say.

When twenty long weeks was over and past
Her mammy asked the reason why she'd thickened round the waist.
It was the pretty ploughboy, the damsel she did say
He caused me to tumble all on the new mown hay.

So good luck to the ploughboy wherever he may be
Who likes to have a lassie to sit upon his knee.
With a jug of good strong beer he'll whistle and he'll sing
And the ploughboy is as happy as a prince or a king.

THE LIGHT OF THE MOON

Tune and text: Hammond D248. Robert Barratt, Piddletown, Dorset. September/October 1905.

Text: Hammond D538. Farmer Mills, Knowle Farm, Beaminster, Dorset. June 1906.

1. Oh once I loved a lass and she lov - ed not me Be - cause I was grown poor, a lit - tle poor, a lit - tle poor But she all in good part has stole a - way my heart And she'll keep it for e - ver - more. *etc.*

2. It was un - der my true-love's win - dow one night *etc.*

3. When I be - held my true love's charms

Oh once I loved a lass and she lovèd not me
Because I was grown poor, a little poor, a little poor
But she all in good part has stole away my heart
And she'll keep it for evermore.

It was under my true-love's window one night
Oh there did I holloa so shrill, o, little shrill, o, little shrill, o.
My true-love arose and slipped on her clothes
And so softaly she let me in.

When I beheld my true-love's charms
My heart grew cold and faint, a little faint, a little faint.
I took her around the middle so small
And carried her to bed again.

Oh 'twas all the first part of the night
We did both sport and play, so pretty play, so pretty play
And all the latter part of the night
She in my arms did lay.

Now her father kept a cock and a pretty crowing cock
And it crowed in the morning so soon, so very soon, so very soon.
My love she thought 'twas day and she hastened me away
But it proved to be the light of the moon.

The wind it did blow and the cocks they did crow
As I tripped o'er the plain, so very plain, so very plain
And I wished myself back in my true-love's arms
And she in her bed again.

Now I'll prove so true to my love as the sun that do shine
Over the fallow ground, the fallow ground, the fallow ground
And if she's not true to me as I am true to she
I would rather she was lost than found.

LIMBO

Gardiner H1275. James Brooman, Upper Faringdon, Hampshire. October 1908.

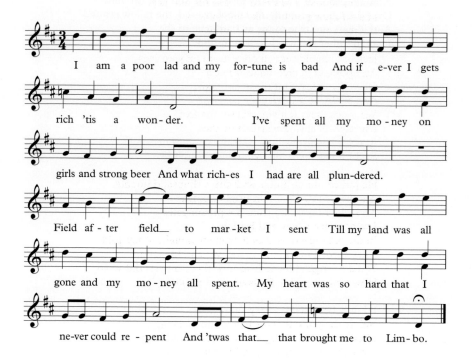

I am a poor lad and my fortune is bad
And if ever I gets rich 'tis a wonder.
I've spent all my money on girls and strong beer
And what riches I had are all plundered.
Field after field to market I sent
Till my land was all gone and my money all spent.
My heart was so hard that I never could repent
And 'twas that that brought me to Limbo.

Once I could run whilst others did lie
And strut like a crow in the gutter.
The people all said that saw me pass by
There goes Mr Fop in a flutter.
To the top and top-gallant I hoisted my sails
With a fine fringy cravat and a wig with three tails
And now I am ready to gnaw my own nails
And drink the cold water of Limbo.

I had an old uncle lived down in the west
And he heard of my sad disaster.
Poor soul, after that he could never take no rest
For his troubles came faster and faster.
He came to the gaol to view my sad case
And as soon as I saw him I knew his old face.
I stood gazing on him like one in amaze
I wished myself safe out of Limbo.

Jack, if I should set you once more on your legs
And put you in credit and fashion
Oh will you leave off those old rakish ways
And try for to govern your passion?
Yes, uncle, says I, if you will set me free
I surely will always be ruled by thee
And I'll labour my bones for the good of my soul
And I'll pay them for laying me in Limbo.

He pulled out his purse with three thousand pounds
And he counted it out in bright guineas
And when I was free from the prison gates
I went to see Peggy and Jeannie.
In my old ragged clothes they knew nought of my gold
They turned me all out in the wet and the cold.
You'd a-laughed for to hear how those hussies did scold
How they jawed me for laying in Limbo.

I'd only been there a very short time
Before my pockets they then fell to picking.
I banged them as long as my cane I could hold
Until they fell coughing and kicking.
The one bawled out, Murder! the other did scold
I banged them as long as my cane I could hold
I banged their old bodies for the good of their souls
And I paid them for laying me in Limbo.

THE LOWLANDS OF HOLLAND

Tune: Gardiner H1086. William Bone, Medstead, Alton, Hampshire. November 1907.

Text: Gardiner H615. Stephen Phillimore, Andover, Hampshire. August 1906.

As I walked out_ one May morn-ing down by a ri-ver - side

There I be-held_ my love-ly fair, oh then to be_ my bride.

Oh_ then to be_ my bride, my boys, and the cham-bers to be - hold.

May the hea-vens a-bove pro - tect my love for a jol-ly sail - or bold.

(a)

hea-vens a-bove pro -

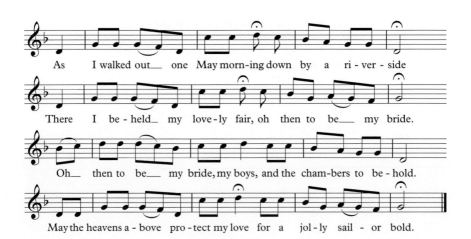

As I walked out_ one May morn-ing down by a ri-ver - side

There I be-held_ my love-ly fair, oh then to be_ my bride.

Oh_ then to be_ my bride, my boys, and the cham-bers to be - hold.

May the heavens a - bove pro-tect my love for a jol-ly sail - or bold.

As I walked out one May morning down by a riverside
There I beheld my lovely fair, oh then to be my bride.
Oh then to be my bride, my boys, and the chambers to behold.
May the heavens above protect my love for a jolly sailor bold.

I will build my love a gallant ship, a ship of noble fame
With a hundred and seventy sailor boys to box her about the main.
With a hundred and seventy sailor boys without any fear or doubt
With my true-love in that gallant ship I was sadly tossed about.

The anchor and the cable went overboard straightway
The mainmast and the rigging lay buried in the sea.
'Twas tempests and bad weather and the raging of the sea
I never, never had but one true-love and he was drowned at sea.

Said the father to the daughter, What makes you so lament?
There is a lad in our town can give you heart content.
There is not a lad in our town, neither lord nor duke, said she
Since the raging sea and the stormy winds parted my love and me.

No handkerchief shall bind my head, no comb go through my hair
No firelight nor candle bright shall view my beauty fair
And neither will I married be until the day I die
Since the raging sea and the stormy winds parted my love and I.

Marrow-Bones

Hammond D394. John Pomery, Bridport Union, Dorset. May 1906.

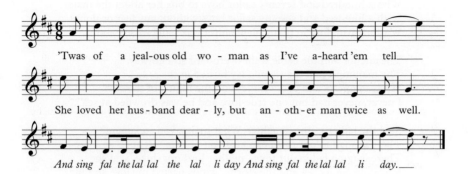

'Twas of a jeal-ous old wo-man as I've a-heard 'em tell____

She loved her hus-band dear-ly, but an-oth-er man twice as well.

And sing fal the lal lal the lal li day And sing fal the lal lal li day.____

'Twas of a jealous old woman as I've a-heard 'em tell
She loved her husband dearly, but another man twice as well.

Chorus: *And sing fal the lal lal the lal li day*
         And sing fal the lal lal li day.

She went unto the doctor to see what she could find
To know what was the very best thing to make her husband blind.

You boil him up some good rum punch, I'm sure that's very good
And stew him up some marrow-bones to circulate his blood.

But this old man being a crafty blade and knowing the scheme before
He drank it up and said, My dear, I can't see you at all.

I'll go down to the river and there myself will drown.
Says she, I'll come along with you in case you should fall down.

Oh they went along both hand in hand till they came to the river's brim
The old man tipped his foot to one side and the old woman went rolling in.

Good Lord! How she did holloa and loud for mercy call
But the old man said, I'm so very blind I can't see you at all.

THE MILLER'S THREE SONS

Gardiner H255. Dr Graham, Bournemouth, Hampshire. May 1906.

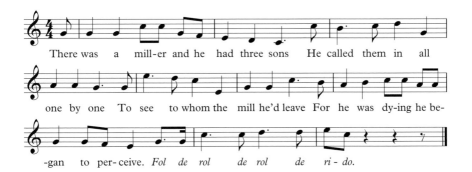

There was a mill-er and he had three sons He called them in all one by one To see to whom the mill he'd leave For he was dy-ing he be--gan to per-ceive. *Fol de rol de rol de ri - do.*

There was a miller and he had three sons
He called them in all one by one
To see to whom the mill he'd leave
For he was dying he began to perceive.

Chorus: *Fol de rol de rol de rido.*

First he called his eldest son
O son, said he, my race is run
And if to thee my mill I'd leave
Pray tell me how you intend to deal.

Father, said he, my name is Jack
Of every bushel I'd steal a peck
Of every bushel one peck I'd steal
And that's the way I intend to deal.

Thou art a fool, the old man said
Thou hast not learned well thy trade.
My mill to thee I'll never give
For by such toll no man can live.

Then he called his second son
O son, said he, my race is run
And if to thee my mill I'd leave
Pray tell me how you intend to deal.

Father, said he, my name is Ralph
Of every bushel I'd steal one half
Of every bushel one half I'd steal
And that's the way I intend to deal.

Thou art a fool, the old man said
Thou hast not learned well thy trade.
My mill to thee I'll never give
For by such toll no man can live.

Then he called his youngest son
O son, said he, my race is run
And if to thee my mill I'd leave
Pray tell me how you intend to deal.

Father, said he, I'm your youngest boy
And stealing corn is all my joy
And rather than the mill should lack
I'll steal all the corn and foreswear
        the sack.

Son, said he, thou art an honest lad
Thy brothers know not half their trade.
I'll leave to thee the mill, he cried
So said his prayers, cocked his toes
        and died.

My Bonny, Bonny Boy

Gardiner H309. George Blake, Bitterne, Southampton, Hampshire. May 1906.

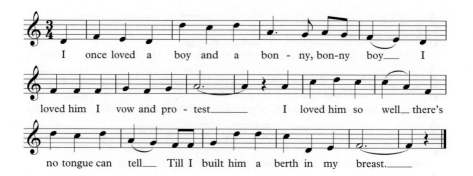

I once loved a boy and a bonny, bonny boy
I loved him I vow and protest
I loved him so well there's no tongue can tell
Till I built him a berth on my breast.

'Twas up the wild forest and through the green groves
Like one that was troubled in mind
I hallooed, I whooped, and I played* on my flute
But no bonny boy could I find.

I looked up high and I looked down low
The weather being wonderful warm
And who should I spy but my own bonny boy
Locked fast in another girl's arms.

He took me upon his assembled knees
And looked me quite hard in the face
He gave unto me one sweet smile and a kiss
But his heart's in another girl's breast.

Now my bonny, bonny boy is across the salt seas
And I hope he will safely return
But if he loves another girl better than me
Let him take her and why should I mourn?

Now the girl that enjoys my own bonny boy
She is not to be blamed I am sure
For many's the long night he have robbed me of my rest
But he never shall do it no more.

*'Blew' in the original edition; this was a reproduction of a
copyist's error in Gardiner's typescript.*

70

MY CHARMING MOLLY O!

Gardiner H256. Dr Graham, Bournemouth, Hampshire. May 1906.

Of__ all the love-ly girls a-bout that I do chance to know

There are none who are half so pret-ty as my charm-ing Mol-ly, o.

She is young, she is beau-ti-ful, she is fair-est of them all

The__ ro-ses in her cheeks I love, she's win-some and she's tall

I will toast her bon-ny self be-fore I rise__ to__ go

For the on-ly one en-ti-ces me is charm-ing Mol-ly, o.

Of all the lovely girls about that I do chance to know
There are none who are half so pretty as my charming Molly, o.

Chorus: *She is young, she is beautiful, she is fairest of them all*
               The roses in her cheeks I love, she's winsome and she's tall
               I will toast her bonny self before I rise to go
               For the only one entices me is charming Molly, o.

But the sweetest flowers will wither and the fruit it will decay
And the beauty of a fair maid may soon pass away.

So I will waste no time, my lads, before to church I go
And wed the fairest lass on earth, my charming Molly, o.

NELLY THE MILKMAID

Hammond D786. Marina Russell, Upwey, Dorset. January/February 1907.

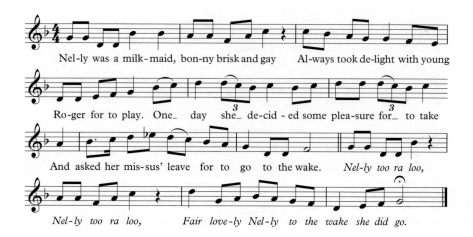

Nel-ly was a milk-maid, bon-ny brisk and gay   Al-ways took de-light with young
Ro-ger for to play.   One_ day   she_ de-cid - ed some plea-sure for_ to take
And asked her mis-sus' leave   for to go to the wake.   *Nel-ly too ra loo,*
Nel-ly too ra loo,   *Fair love-ly Nel-ly to the wake she did go.*

Nelly was a milkmaid, bonny brisk and gay
Always took delight with young Roger for to play.
One night she decided some pleasure for to take
And asked her missus' leave for to go to the wake.

Chorus: *Nelly too ra loo, Nelly too ra loo,*
           Fair lovely Nelly to the wake she did go.

O Nelly, said her missus, I'd have you to take care
And of that young rogue, Roger, I'd have you to beware
So, Nelly, you may go, but this promise you must make
Do not frolic with young Roger coming home from the wake.

So dressed all in her best young Nelly did repair
And as she expected, young Roger he was there.
They danced and they sang, they had beer, ale and cake
And many were the pleasures that they had at the wake.

The wake being over, they homeward went their way
Until they came to the new cocks of hay
Then Roger kissed young Nelly and her promise she did break
And she frolicked with young Roger coming home from the wake.

When eight months were over and nine coming on
Young Nelly was the mother of a fine lovely son.
I will call it, said she, I will call it for his sake
I will call it Young Roger Coming Home from the Wake.

NIGHTINGALES SING

Hammond D138. William Bartlett, Wimbourne Union, Dorset. August 1905.

As I was a-walking one morning in May
Oh there I saw a young couple a-making of hay
Oh and one was a pretty maid and her beauty shone clear
And the other was a soldier in the bold Grenadiers.

A-walking and a-talking and a-walking together
Oh a-walking so far about till they couldn't tell whither
So they sat themselves down by the clear crystal stream
Oh all for to see the flowers grow and hear the nightingales sing.

Then with kisses and compliments he took her round the middle
And out of his knapsack he drawed forth a fiddle
And he played her such a fine tune as made the groves and valleys ring
Oh 'tis Hark, hark, says the fair maid, how the nightingales sing.

Oh come then, said the soldier, it is time to give o'er.
Oh no, then said the fair maid, we will have one tune more.
I do so like the music and the tune of your string
I do like to see the flowers grow and hear the nightingales sing.

Then come, said the fair maid, will you marry me?
Oh no, then said the soldier, oh that never can be
For I have got a wife in my own counterie
And so fair a woman that ever you did see.

Oh no, then said the soldier, oh that never can be
For I have got a wife there and childeren three
But if I should come this way again, oh 'twill be in the spring
I will come and see the flowers grow and hear the nightingales sing.

THE NOBLEMAN'S WEDDING

Hammond D429. Mrs Crawford, West Milton, Dorset. May 1906.

Yesterday evening I was invited to
a wedding
'Twas of a fair girl that proved so unkind.
Although she had decided to wed
with another
'Twas her former lover still run in her mind.

When supper was over and all things
were ended
They all did conclude to give the bride
a song.
The first that begun was a farmer, her
old lover
And the song that he sang it was not
very long.

Oh how can you sit at another man's table?
How can you drink of another man's wine?
How can you lie on another man's pillow
When once you were a true lover of mine?

How can you sleep on another man's
bosom
Since you pretend that you love me so dear?
Now for your sweet sake I'll wear the
mournful willow
Now and for ever I'll wear it my dear.

The bride she was sitting at the head of
the table
Hearing these words she marked them
right well.
It pierced her heart till she could no longer
stand it
Down at the feet of the bridegroom she fell.

Now I am going to ask of you one favour
I hope that the same you will grant unto me
'Tis all this long night let me lie with
my mother
The rest of my life I will lie along with thee.

The favour was granted and all things
were ready
With sighing and crying they all went
to bed.
'Twas early next morning this young
man arose
When he went to her chamber he found
she was dead.

He picked her up in his bosom so softly
He carried her into the garden again
He covered her over with flowers so sweetly
Hoping to revive her, but all 'twas in vain.

All round my hat I will wear the mournful willow
All round my hat for a twelvemonth or more
But if I should find that it does not become me
Then I'll leave it off for ever and evermore.

No, Sir, No

Tune (a) and text: Hammond D417. John Greening, Cuckold's Corner, Dorset. May 1906.
Tune (b) and text: Hammond D880. Mrs Bowring, Cerne Abbas, Dorset. December 1907.

Pret-ty maid walk-ing in the_ gar-den Who she is I__ do not know.

I'll go__court her for her_beau-ty Let the an-swer be Yes or No.

Oh dear, oh! No, sir, no! Still her an-swer to me was, No!

Pret-ty maid walk-ing in the gar-den Who she is I do not know.

I'll go court her for her beau-ty Let the an-swer be Yes or No.

Oh dear, oh! No, sir,_ no! Still her an-swer to me was, No!

Pretty maid walking in the garden
Who she is I do not know.
I'll go court her for her beauty
Let the answer be Yes or No.

Chorus: *Oh dear, oh! No, sir, no!*
          Still her answer to me was, No!

Madam I am come a-courting
Hoping your favour I shall gain
If you'll kindly entertain me
Perhaps some day I'll call again.

My husband is a Spanish captain
Left me to mourn three weeks ago.
The very last time we kissed and parted
He told me, Always answer, No!

Lady walking in the garden
No aloner might you be.
If I should walk along beside you
Would that be any harm to thee?

Stooping down to tie her garter
Just a little above her knee
If my hand should slide any farther
Would that be any harm to thee?

So they lay all night together
Till the cocks begin to crow.
Now the daylight is appearing
Open your arms and let me go.

There's one more thing I have to ask you
That's before I let you go
Did you ever sleep more sweeter
Was you ever cuddled so?

NOTHING AT ALL

Hammond D261. Robert Barratt, Piddletown, Dorset. September/October 1905.

Oh a song a-bout no-thing I'll sing But a sto-ry of some-thing I'll tell.

I'll tell you what no-thing do mean And how of-ten-times it do ex - cel.___

How of-ten we're put to a shift How of-ten we quar-rel and brawl

But if none of us are in the right Then it's

all a-bout no-thing at all. *And sing fal the ral lal the li day.*___

Oh a song about nothing I'll sing
But a story of something I'll tell.
I'll tell you what nothing do mean
And how oftentimes it do excel.
How often we're put to a shift
How often we quarrel and brawl
But if none of us are in the right
Then it's all about nothing at all.

Chorus: *And sing fal the ral lal the li day.*

Now a miser will lay up his store
And often he gains an increase
But he never enjoys it himself
He knows neither blessing or peace.
For money brings trouble, you see
And trouble brings sorrow withal
And those that from sorrow be free
Is them that has nothing at all.

Now a man that has got a bad wife
And she with him quarrel and tease
Will harry him out of his life
So he'd better by far hold his peace.
For at length she must spend her breath
And then she must surely fall
For when she is conquered by death
Then she can say nothing at all.

Now fill this glass up to the brim
And let not one drop of it fall
And drink a good health unto me
That do sing about nothing at all.
And now, my companions gay
I'd have you the reckoning call
For you've all got a shilling to pay
For I have got nothing at all.

OLD GREY BEARD A-WAGGING

Gardiner H1305. Henry Purkiss, Cadnam, Hampshire. October 1908.

There was an old man came over the lea
Oh have him? I won't have him!
Come over the lea to get married to me
With his old grey beard a-wagging.

My mother she bade me go open the door
I opened the door and he fell on the floor.

My mother she bade me go get him a stool
I got him a stool and he sat like a fool.

My mother she bade me go sit on his knee
I sat on his knee and he tried to kiss me.

My mother she bade me go get him some gin
I got him some gin and by Jove how he grinned!

My mother she bade me go light him to bed
I lit him to bed and he asked me to wed.

My mother she bade me go take him to church
I took him to church and left him in the lurch.

An Old Man Came Courting Me

Gardiner H1061. Mrs Davey, Alresford Workhouse, Hampshire. November 1907.

An old man came courting me
Heigh down derry down
An old man came courting me
Heigh derry down
An old man came courting me
All for to ruin me
Girls, for your sakes never wed an old man.

When this old man comes to bed
Heigh down derry down
When this old man comes to bed
Heigh derry down
When this old man comes to bed
He lays like a lump of lead
Girls, for your sakes never wed an old man.

When this old man goes to sleep
Heigh down derry down
When this old man goes to sleep
Heigh derry down
When this old man goes to sleep
Out of bed I do creep
Into the arms of some jolly young man.

I wish this old man would die
Heigh down derry down
I wish this old man would die
Heigh derry down
I wish this old man would die
I'd make his money fly
Girls, for your sakes never wed an old man.

A young man is my delight
Heigh down derry down
A young man is my delight
Heigh derry down
A young man is my delight
He'll kiss you day and night
Girls, for your sakes never wed an old man.

ONE MAN SHALL SHEAR MY WETHERS

Hammond H709. Mrs Stone, Dorchester Union, Dorset. December 1906.

×These two notes are repeated in the second verse, sung three times in the third verse, and so on up to ten.

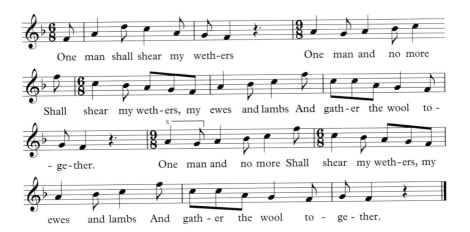

One man shall shear my wethers
One man and no more
Shall shear my wethers, my ewes and lambs
And gather the wool together.
One man and no more
Shall shear my wethers, my ewes and lambs
And gather the wool together.

Two men shall shear my wethers
Two men and no more
Shall shear my wethers, my ewes and lambs
And gather the wool together.
One man, two men and no more
Shall shear my wethers, my ewes and lambs
And gather the wool together.

Three men shall shear my wethers
Three men and no more
Shall shear my wethers, my ewes and lambs
And gather the wool together.
One man, two men, three men and no more
Shall shear my wethers, my ewes and lambs
And gather the wool together.

Proceeding in this fashion up to ten men, and then returning backwards (counting backwards as well) until one is reached.

THE PENNY WAGER

Gardiner H878. William Tod, Portsmouth Workhouse, Hampshire. August 1907.

As I tra-velled from the North Coun-try___ Seek-ing for good com-pa-ny
It was_good com-pa-ny I___ did find_There's no-thing to e-qual it to my mind.
Sing-ing fol le did-dle le-ro, rite fol le day Whilst I in my pock-et had one pen-ny.

As I travelled from the North Country
Seeking for good company
It was good company I did find
There's nothing to equal it to my mind.

Chorus: *Singing fol le diddle lero, rite fol le day*
Whilst I in my pocket had one penny.

Oh I saw two gentlemen playing at dice
They took me to be some young nobleman nice
As they sat a-playing and I looking on
They took me to be some nobleman's son.

They asked of me if I would play
I asked of them what bets they did lay.
The one said a guinea, the other ten pound
The bargain was made but no money laid down.

I took up the dice and gave it a spin
It was my good fortune that time to win.
If I had a-lost and not had a-won
I should have had to throw my empty purse down.

I stopped there that night and part of next day
When I thought it quite time to be jogging away.
I asked the landlady what was to pay
She said, Give us a kiss, love, and then on your way!

THE PLOUGHBOY'S DREAM

Gardiner H748. Daniel Wigg, Preston Candover, Alresford, Hampshire. July 1907.

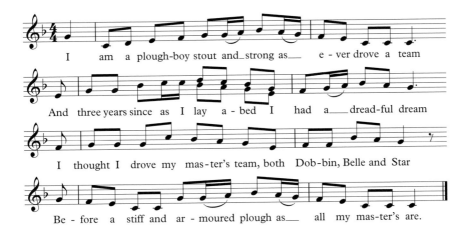

I am a ploughboy stout and strong as ever drove a team
And three years since as I lay abed I had a dreadful dream
I thought I drove my master's team, both Dobbin, Belle and Star
Before a stiff and armoured plough as all my master's are.

I found the ground was baked so hard 'twas more like bricks than clay
I could not cut my furrow through, nor would my beasts obey.
The more I whipped them, slashed and swore, the less my horses tried
Dobbin lay down, and Belle and Star ignored my threats and cries.

Till lo! above me appeared a youth, he seemed to hang in air
And all around a dazzling light which made my eyes to stare.
Give over, cruel wretch, he cried, do not thy beasts abuse
Think if the ground was not so hard they would their work refuse?

Besides I heard thee curse and swear as if dumb beasts could know
What all thy oaths and cursing meant, it's better far than gold
That you should know that there is one who knows thy sins full well
And what shall be thy after doom another shall thee tell.

No more he said, but light as air he vanished from my sight
And with him went the sun's bright beams, 'twas all as dark as night.
The thunder roared from underground, the earth it seemed to gape
Blue flames broke forth and in those flames appeared an awful shape.

I soon shall call thee mine, he cried, with a voice so clear and deep
And quivering like an aspen leaf I woke out of my sleep.
So ponder well, you ploughboys all, this dream that I have told
And if the work goes hard with you, it's worth your weight in gold.

POLLY VAUGHAN

Tune and text: Gardiner H1087. William Bone, Medstead, Alton, Hampshire. November 1907.

Tune variants and text: Gardiner H1175. Mrs Matthews, Hampshire (exact locality unknown). August 1908.

One Midsummer's evening the sun being gone down
Young Polly went a-walking by the side of a pond.
She sat under a shady tree a shower for to shun
With her apron wrapped around her as white as a swan.

Young William went a-hunting with his dog and his gun
Young William went a-hunting as the evening came on.
Down among those green rushes as the evening came on
Young William shot his true-love in the room of a swan.

He throwed down his gun and away he did run
Crying, Father, dear father, can you believe what I've done?
Down among those green rushes as the evening came on
I shot my own true-love in the room of a swan.

Stay at home, my dearest William, till your trial do come on
That you may not be banished to some foreign land.
On the day of your trial your father will appear
With fifty bright guineas if that will you clear.

On the day of his trial young Polly did appear
Crying, People, o people, let William go clear.
With my apron wrapped around my head as the evening came on
He shot his own true-love in the room of a swan.

THE POOR OLD COUPLE

Hammond D714. Mrs Seale, Dorchester Union, Dorset. December 1906.

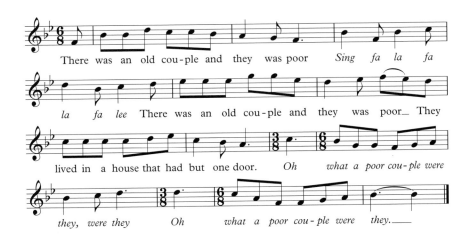

There was an old cou-ple and they was poor *Sing fa la fa la fa lee* There was an old cou-ple and they was poor_ They lived in a house that had but one door. *Oh what a poor cou-ple were they, were they Oh what a poor cou-ple were they.___*

There was an old couple and they
  was poor
Sing fa la fa la fa lee
There was an old couple and they
  was poor
They lived in a house that had but
  one door.
  Oh what a poor couple were they,
  were they
  Oh what a poor couple were they.

The old man he went far from home
The old woman was 'fraid to
  stay alone.
  Oh what a weak woman
  was she, etc.

The clerk of the parish he lived close by
And he was resolved with th'old woman
  to lie.
  Oh what a bold man was he, etc.

At eight o'clock or a little more
A gentle knock came to the door.
  Oh who is this? said she, etc.

It's only the clerk, come don't be afraid
Come down and open the door, he said.
  Oh yes I will, said she.

At ten o'clock or a little more
Another knock came to the door.
  Oh who is there? said she, etc.

It's only your husband, come don't be
afraid
Come down and open the door, he said.
  Oh yes, in a minute, said she, etc.

It's I've been sick since you've been gone
If you'd been in the garden you'd a-heard
  me groan.
  I'm sorry for that, said he, etc.

There's one thing I'll request of thee
Go fetch me an apple from yonder tree.
  That's easily done, said he, etc.

The old man he climbed up the tree
Out pops the clerk and away runs he.
  That's cleverly done, said she, etc.

THE RAMBLING SOLDIER

Gardiner H216. George Digweed, Micheldever, Hampshire. March 1906.

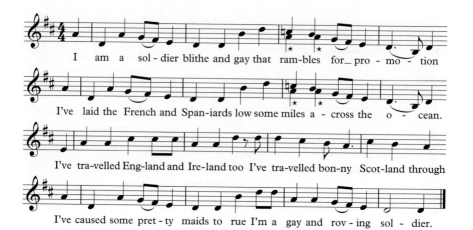

I am a soldier blithe and gay that rambles for promotion
I've laid the French and Spaniards low some miles across the ocean.
I've travelled England and Ireland too
I've travelled bonny Scotland through
I've caused some pretty maids to rue
I'm a gay and roving soldier.

When I was young and in my prime twelve years I went recruiting
Through England, Ireland, Scotland too, wherever I was suiting
With a lady gay and a spendful life
And every town a different wife
Seldom was there any strife
With a gay and roving soldier.

At Woolwich Town I courted Jane, her sister and her mother
And all the time that I was there they was jealous of each other.
Our orders came, I had to start
I left poor Jane with a broken heart
From Woolwich town we soon did part
With a gay and roving soldier.

The Queen she has commanded me to range the country over
From Woolwich Town to Liverpool, from Plymouth back to Dover.
In whatever town I went
To court all damsels I was bent
And to marry none was my intent
But still be a roving soldier.

Now the wars they're at an end and I am not ashamed to mention
The Queen has given me my discharge and granted me a pension.
No doubt some lasses will me blame
But none of them can tell my name
But if you want to know the same
It's Bill* the roving soldier.

*or insert the name of your choice, as suggested in the original edition.

RAP-A-TAP-TAP

Gardiner H50. John Carter, Twyford, Hampshire. June 1905.

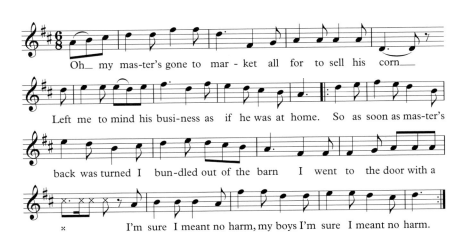

Oh my master's gone to market all for to sell his corn
Left me to mind his business as if he was at home.
So as soon as master's back was turned I bundled out of the barn
I went to the door with a x-x-x-x!* I'm sure I meant no harm, my boys
I'm sure I meant no harm.

> *So as soon as master's back was turned I bundled out of the barn*
> *I went to the door with a x-x-x-x! I'm sure I meant no harm, my boys*
> *I'm sure I meant no harm.*

Soon as my missus heard me she quickly let me in
And she asked me if I was a-dry, my boys, she brought to me some gin
And I was to drink it up, my boys, and never a word to be said
That I'd been there with a x-x-x-x! Straightway we went to bed, my boys
Straightway we went to bed.
       And I was to drink it up, etc.

We hadn't been in bed but a half an hour or more
Before she played me so pretty a tune I thought she'd never give o'er
Saying, you've won my heart for ever, your master's no man for me
For he can't come with a x-x-x-x! not half so well as thee, my boys
Not half so well as thee.
       Saying, you've won my heart for ever, etc.

So my master come from market and he asked me what I'd done.
I told him I'd minded his business as though he'd been at home
So he ordered me some beer, my boys, but little did he know
That I'd been there with a x-x-x-x! or else he'd never done so, my boys
Or else he'd never done so.
       So he ordered me some beer, etc.

So come all you frolicking fellows wherever you may be
I'd have you come with a x-x-x-x! when your master's out of the way
When your master he's a-crossing the flowery fields in May
I'd have you come with a x-x-x-x! Oh let it be night or day, my boys
Oh let it be night or day.
       When your master he's a-crossing, etc.

˟ *x-x-x-x! the rhythm is beaten out on any convenient bar counter, table, etc.*

ROGER'S COURTSHIP

Gardiner H487. Mrs North, Dummer, Basingstoke, Hampshire. August 1906.

Now Roger, my son, just listen to me
And I'll give you good counsel for life
Put on your best clothes and your very best hose
And I'll warrant you'll get you a wife, you will
Yes you will, so you will, and I'll warrant you'll get you a wife, you will.

So Roger put on his very best clothes
Which neither were tattered nor torn
And to match with his clothes he had new yellow hose
And he looked like a gentleman born, he did
Yes he did, so he did, he looked like a gentleman born, he did.

The very first damsel he happened to meet
Was the farmer's fine daughter named Grace
But before he had whispered three words in her ear
She gave him a slap in the face, she did
Yes she did, so she did, she gave him a slap in the face, she did.

As Roger was walking along the street
Admiring of all the fine folks
He happened to kiss the wife of the priest
And she had him put in the stocks, she did
Yes she did, so she did, and she had him put in the stocks, she did.

If these are the troubles of seeking a wife
I'll never look after another
But I will live single the rest of my life
And I will go home to my mother, I will
Yes I will, so I will, and I will go home to my mother, I will.

THE SAILOR DECEIVED

Hammond D408. John Pomery, Bridport Union, Dorset. May 1906.

As I was walking up London Street
I found a letter betwixt my feet
And down to the bottom these lines were wrote
A single sailor is soon forgot.

I went unto my love's father's hall
And boldly for my true-love did call
And her father asked me what I did mean
'Twas so long time she'd married been.

I've neither gold nor I've neither crown
But I'll sail the ocean all round and round.
I'll sail the ocean until I die
I don't care where my poor body lie.

Serious Tom

Gardiner H950. James Channon, Ellisfield, Basingstoke, Hampshire. September 1907.

Here's ser-i-ous Tom sits o-ver his bowl With his pipe and his pot for to cheer his soul While his gay com-pa-ni-ons a-round him cling He'll muse a-while and_ then he'll sing He'll muse a-while and_ then he'll sing: A sin-gle life is a life of joy There's no girl on earth shall my peace des-troy For I'll laugh and joke_ and_ drink and sing And live as_ hap-py_ as a king. For while we are loved by our friends all a-round There's no great-er_ plea-sure can be found.

Here's serious Tom sits over his bowl
With his pipe and his pot for to cheer his soul
While his gay companions around him cling
He'll muse awhile and then he'll sing
He'll muse awhile and then he'll sing:

Chorus: *A single life is a life of joy*
              There's no girl on earth shall my peace destroy
              For I'll laugh and joke and drink and sing
              And live as happy as a king.
              For while we are loved by our friends all around
              There's no greater pleasure can be found
              There's no greater pleasure can be found.

I own I love a single life
Though there's many lives happy with a wife
But when all is said and all is done
The hazard is too great to run
The hazard is too great to run.

THE SHEEP-SHEARING SONG

Hammond D358. William Miller, Wooton Fitzpaine, Dorset. April 1906.

Here's the rosebud in June, the sweet violets in bloom
And the birds singing gaily on ev'ry green bough
The pink and the lily and the daffy-down-dilly
To adorn and perfume the sweet meadows in June.

Chorus: *Whilst out the plough, the fat oxen go slow*
           And the lads and the lasses a-sheep-shearing go.

Here's the cleanly milk pail is full of brown ale
Our table, our table, our table we'll spread
We will sit and we'll drink, we'll laugh, joke and sing
Each lad takes his lass out on the green grass.

Now the shepherds have sheared all their jolly, jolly sheep
What joy can be greater than to talk of the increase.
Here's the ewes and the lambs, the hogs and the rams
The fat wethers too, they'll make a fine show.

SHEPHERDS' SONG

Tune and text (verse 1): Gardiner H1224. William Cole, East Stratton, Micheldever,
Hampshire. September 1908.

Text: Gardiner H718. Moses Mills, Preston Candover, Alresford, Hampshire. July 1907.

Text: Gardiner H647. Benjamin Arnold, Easton, Winchester, Hampshire. November 1906.

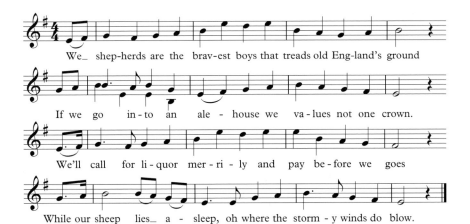

We shepherds are the bravest boys that treads old England's ground
If we go into an ale-house we values not one crown.
We'll call for liquor merrily and pay before we goes
While our sheep lies asleep, oh where the stormy winds do blow.

Come all you valiant shepherds that have got valiant hearts
That goes out in the morning and never feels the smart
We'll never be faint-hearted, we'll fear no frost or snow
We will work in the fields, oh where the stormy winds do blow.

As I looked out all on the hill it made my heart to bleed
To see my sheep hang out their tongues and they began to bleat
And I plucked up my courage bold and up the hill did go
To drive them to the fold, oh where stormy winds do blow.

And now I have a-folded them and 'turned back again
I'll join some jovial company and there be entertained
A-drinking of strong liquor, boys, which is our heart's delight
While our sheep lies asleep, oh full safely all this night.

THE SHOEMAKER'S KISS

Tune and refrain: Hammond D625. William Bartlett, Wimborne Union, Dorset.
September 1906.

Text: Hammond D346. George Bowditch, Charmouth, Dorset. March 1906.

There was an old woman lived down in the west
So green as the leaves they are green, green, green, green
So green as the leaves they are green
And she had a fine daughter that never was kissed
And you know very well what I mean, mean, mean, mean
You know very well what I mean.

One morning she rose and she put on her clothes,
And away to the shoemaker's shop she did go.

Shoemaker, shoemaker, have you got any shoes?
Why, yes, pretty maiden, I think I'll fit you.

So into the shoemaker's shop she did trip.
Good Lord! How he caught her and kissed her sweet lips.

When twenty long weeks they were over and past
This silly young girl she grew thick round the waist.

When forty long weeks were over and done,
This little bold wench had a big, bonny son.

O daughter, o daughter, how come you by this?
O mother, o mother, 'twas the shoemaker's kiss.

THE SOLDIER'S PRAYER

Gardiner H254. Dr Graham, Bournemouth, Hampshire. May 1906.

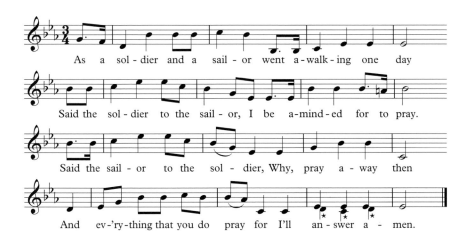

As a soldier and a sailor went a-walking one day
Said the soldier to the sailor, I be a-minded for to pray.
Said the sailor to the soldier, Why, pray away then
And ev'rything that you do pray for I'll answer amen.

The first thing we'll pray for will be lots of strong beer
That we may have plenty our hearts for to cheer
That for every one pint now that we may have ten
And we always, always shall be happy. Said the sailor, Amen!

The next thing we'll pray for will be lots of good baccy
That we may have plenty for to make us both happy
That for every one pipe now that we may have ten
And we always, always shall be happy. Said the sailor, Amen!

The next thing we'll pray for will be for our wives
That we may live happily all the days of our lives
That for every one kiss now that we may have ten
And we always, always shall be happy. Said the sailor, Amen!

The last thing we'll pray for it'll be when we dies
That we may be carried up beyond the blue skies
And when you and I, Bill, we meets up in heaven
We'll have our wives, our pipes and beer and baccy.
            Said the sailor, Amen!

THE SOLDIER AND HIS TRUE-LOVE

Tune and text: Hammond D622. Mrs Bartlett, Halstock Leigh, Dorset. July 1906.

Text: Hammond D623. Mrs Courtenay, Higher Bockhampton, Dorset. September 1906.

The soldier and his true-love walked out one summer's day
To view the flowers and the meadows so gay
While the blackbirds and the thrushes sang on every green spray
And the larks sang so melodious at the dawn of the day.
> *And the larks sang so melodious*
> *And the larks sang so melodious*
> *And the larks sang so melodious*
> *At the dawn of the day.*

Now as this young couple their pleasure did take
Said the soldier to his true-love, I must you forsake.
I am bound to the Indies where the loud cannons roar
I must go and leave my Nancy, she's the girl I adore.
> *I must go and leave my Nancy, etc.*

Three heavy sighs she gave, saying, Jimmy, my dear
And are you a-going to leave me in sorrow and despair?
And are you a-going to leave me in sorrow to complain
Till you from the Indies return back again?
> *Till you from the Indies, etc.*

A ring from her finger she instantly drew
Saying, Take this, darling Jimmy, and more I'll give you
And as she embraced him, tears from her eyes did flow
Saying, May I go along with you? Oh no, my love, no.
Saying, May I go along with you, etc.

Farewell, dearest Nancy, I must did you adieu.
The big ship is waiting for to collect up her crew.
I am bound for the ocean on a sweet pleasant tide
And if ever I return again I will make you my bride.
And if ever I return again, etc.

An S-O-N-G

Gardiner H696. Alfred Stride, Dibden, Southampton, Hampshire. June 1907.

As I was a-walk-ing one morn-ing in May I heard a fair dam-sel to sigh and to say My false love has left me and showed me false play 'Twas down in the mea-dows a-mong the green hay.

As I was a-walking one morning in May
I heard a fair damsel to sigh and to say
My false love has left me and showed me false play
'Twas down in the meadows among the green hay.

The very first time that he came to court me
He said he'd be constant in every degree.
The very second time I did him espy
'Twas, Oh no, oh no, my love, not I!

My father is worth five hundred a year
I, being his daughter, his on-e-ly heir.
Not one penny of portion will he give me I fear
If I marries with Y-O-U, my dear.

But as for your portion, my dear, never mind
I'll make you a husband most loving and kind.
So unto the church, love, let us repair
It's never mind your F-A-T-H-E-R.

To church they went and were married straightway
And home to her father's that very same day
Saying, Father, honoured father, I will tell unto thee
We're M-A-double-R-I-E-D.

With that the old man he begin for to swear
Saying, You've married my daughter, my on-e-ly heir
But since it is so, I have a new son
You're W-E-double-L-C-O-M.

SOUR GRAPES

Gardiner H913. Dr Graham, Bournemouth, Hampshire. May 1906.

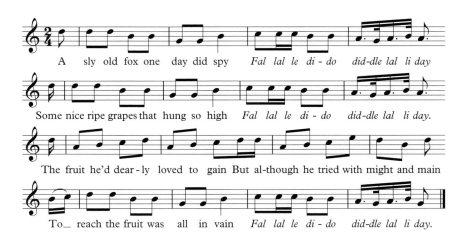

A sly old fox one day did spy *Fal lal le di - do did-dle lal li day*

Some nice ripe grapes that hung so high *Fal lal le di - do did-dle lal li day.*

The fruit he'd dear - ly loved to gain But al-though he tried with might and main

To_ reach the fruit was all in vain *Fal lal le di - do did-dle lal li day.*

A sly old fox one day did spy
    Fal lal le dido diddle lal li day
Some nice ripe grapes that hung so high
    Fal lal le dido diddle lal li day.
The fruit he'd dearly loved to gain
But although he tried with might and main
To reach the fruit was all in vain
    Fal lal le dido diddle lal li day.

The fox his patience nearly lost
    Fal lal le dido diddle lal li day
His expectations black and cross
    Fal lal le dido diddle lal li day.
Still licked his chops for near an hour
Till he found the fruit beyond his power
Then he went and swore the grapes were sour
    Fal lal le dido diddle lal li day.

THE SPRIG OF THYME

Tune and text: Gardiner H270. Moses Blake, Emery Down, Lyndhurst, Hampshire. May 1906.
Text (verses 1, 4, 5): Gardiner H547. David Marlow, Basingstoke, Hampshire. September 1906.

Come all you maid-ens fair That are just now in your prime
I'd have you keep your gar-dens clean And let no man steal your thyme.

Come all you maidens fair
That are just now in your prime
I'd have you keep your gardens
        clean
And let no man steal your thyme.

Oh I once had a sprig of thyme
And it flourished by night and by day
Till at length there came a false
        young man
And he stole my thyme all away.

So now my thyme is all gone
And I cannot plant any new
For the very place where my thyme
        used to grow
Is all overrun with rue.

And rue is a running, running root
And it runs so far underneath
That I will pluck that running,
        running root
And I'll plant a jolly oak tree.

Now here stands the jolly oak tree
That will neither wither or die
And I'll prove so true to my
        dear love
As the stars all in the sky.

The gardener was standing by
I asked him to choose for me.
He chose me the primrose, the violet
        and the vine
But I did them overlook all three.

In June there's a red rosy bud
But that's not the flower for me
For oftentimes I've plucked at the red
        rosy bud
And gained the willow tree.

Green willow it will twist
Green willow it will twine.
I wish that I was safe all in that young
        man's arms
That stole away my thyme.

Green willow I will sing
Green willow shall be my song
That all the world may
        plainly see
That I once loved a false young man.

SWANSEA TOWN

Gardiner H67. William Randall, Hursley, Hampshire. June 1905.

Oh farewell to you, my Nancy, ten thousand times adieu
I'm bound to cross the ocean, girl, once more to part from you.
Once more to part from you, fine girl, you're the girl that I adore
But still I live in hopes to see old Swansea Town once more.

Chorus: *Old Swansea Town once more, fine girl, you're the girl that I adore*
            But still I live in hopes to see old Swansea Town once more.

Oh it's now that I am out at sea and you are far behind
Kind letters I will write to you with the secrets of my mind.
The secrets of my mind, fine girl, you're the girl that I adore
But still I live in hopes to see old Swansea Town once more.

Oh now the storm is rising, I can see it coming on
The night as dark as anything, we cannot see the moon.
Our good old ship she's tossed about, our rigging is all tore
But still I live in hopes to see old Swansea Town once more.

Oh now the storm it's over and we are safe on shore
We'll drink strong drinks and brandies too, to the girls that we adore.
To the girls that we adore, fine girls, we will make this tavern roar
And when our money is all gone, we'll go to sea for more.

THE TAILOR AND THE CROW

Hammond D136. William Bartlett, Wimborne Union, Dorset. 1905.

Now one Mid-sum-mer's morn-ing as I was a-walk-ing *Fal de lal the did-dle lal the li do* One Mid-sum-mers's morn-ing as I was a-walk-ing *Fal de lal the did-dle lal the li do* One Mid-sum-mer's morn-ing as I was a-walk-ing The birds be-gan to whis-tle, o, and I be-gan to sing To my heigh! ho! the car-ri-on crow cries Pork! Be-a-con! Pork! Be-a-con! Oh fal de lal the did-dle lal the li do.

Now one Midsummer's morning as I was a-walking
Fal de lal the diddle lal the li do
One Midsummer's morning as I was a-walking
Fal de lal the diddle lal the li do
One Midsummer's morning as I was a-walking
The birds began to whistle, o, and I began to sing

Chorus: *To my heigh! ho! the carrion crow cries*
              Pork! Be-a-con! Pork! Be-a-con!
              Oh fal de lal the diddle lal the li do.

Now that false carrion crow he stands upon an oak
And he swears he sees a tailor a-cutting out a cloak.

O wife, go and fetch me my arrow and my bow
That I may go shoot at that false carrion crow.

The tailor he shot and he just missed the mark
And he shot the old dairyman's sow right through the heart.

O wife, go and fetch me some treacle in a spoon
For the dairyman's old sow's in a damn poor tune.

Now the old sow she died and the bell begins to toll
And the little pigs are screeching for the old sow's soul.

But the tailor now he says he don't care a louse
For now he's got black-puddings and chitterlings in the house.

THE TAILOR'S BREECHES

Tune and text (verse 1): Hammond D238. Robert Barratt, Piddletown, Dorset. 1905.
Text: Hammond D95. Jacob Baker, Bere Regis, Dorset.

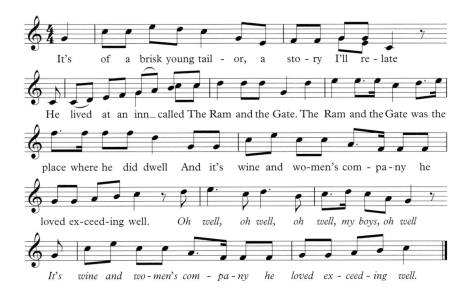

It's of a brisk young tailor, a story I'll relate
He lived at an inn called The Ram and the Gate.
The Ram and the Gate was the place where he did dwell
And it's wine and women's company he loved exceeding well.
> *Oh well, oh well, oh well, my boys, oh well*
> *It's wine and women's company he loved exceeding well.*

Now this tailor he'd been drinking a glass or two of wine
And not being used to drink it caused his face to shine.
It caused his face to shine just like the rising sun
And he swore he'd have a bonny lass before he did go home.
> *Go home, go home, etc.*

So he took her in his arms and he called her his dear honey
And as they both were talking, she was fingering of his money
She was fingering of his money when the tailor smiled and said
If you'll lend me your petticoats I'll dance like a maid.
> *A maid, a maid, etc.*

The tailor pulled his breeches off and the petticoats put on
The tailor danced a dance and the lassie sang a song.
The tailor danced a dance and they played a pretty tune
And they danced the tailor's breeches right out of the room.
> *The room, the room, etc.*

Oh have you ever seen a tailor undone as I'm undone?
My watch and my money and my breeches are all gone.
And now I am undone, I'm become a garden flower
And if ever I get my breeches back I'll never dance no more.
> *No more, no more, etc.*

101

THORNABY WOODS

Hammond Wr298. Mrs Webb, Kings Norton, Worcestershire. February 1906.

In Thorn-a-by woods in Not-ting-ham-shire *Right fa la ra, right fa lad-di-ty*
In Thorn-a-by woods in Not-ting-ham-shire *Fa the ra la ra lee___*
Three keep-ers' hou-ses stood three-square A-bout a mile from each o-ther they were
Their or-ders were to look af-ter the deer. *Right fa the ra la the ra lee.___*

In Thornaby woods in Nottinghamshire
    Right fa la ra, right fa laddity
In Thornaby woods in Nottinghamshire
    Fa the ra la ra lee
Three keepers' houses stood three-square
About a mile from each other they were
Their orders were to look after the deer.
    Right fa the ra la the ra lee.

Me and my dogs went out one night
The moon and stars was shining bright
Over hedges, ditches, fields and stiles
With my three dogs all at my heels
To catch a fat buck in Thornaby fields.

That very first night I had bad luck
For one of my very best dogs got shot.
He came to me both bloody and lame
Sorry was I for to see the same
Him not being able to follow the game.

I looked at his wounds and found them slight
'Twas done by some keeper out of spite.
I'll take my pikestaff in my hand
And I'll search the woods till I find that man
I'll tan his old hide right well if I can.

Then I went home and went to bed
And Limping Jack went out in my stead.
He searched the woods all round and round
Till he found a fat buck lying dead on the ground
'Twas my little dog gave him his death wound.

He took his knife and cut the buck's throat
Then he took some string and tied the buck's legs.
You would ha' laughed to see Limping Jack
Go hopping along with the buck on his back
He carried it like some Yorkshireman's pack.

We got a butcher to skin the game
Likewise another to sell the same.
The very first joint we offered for sale
Was to an old woman who sold bad ale
She had us all up to Nottingham gaol.

Now Nottingham 'sizes are drawing nigh
Where us three chaps have got to be tried.
The gentlemen laughed them all to scorn
That such an old bugger should be foresworn
All into little pieces she ought to a-been torn.

Now Nottingham 'sizes are over and past
And us three chaps got clear at last.
Now the bucks and does shall never go free
For a poaching life is the life for me
And a poacher I will always be.

THE THREE BUTCHERS

Tune: Hammond S288. William Cousins, Bath, Somerset. January 1906.

Text: Hammond D666. Frank Stockley, Wareham, Dorset. November 1906.

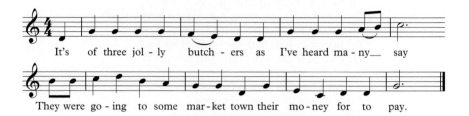

It's of three jolly butchers as I've heard many say
They were going to some market town their money for to pay.

They rode together for a mile or two and a little more beside.
Said Johnson unto Jipson, I heard a woman cry.

Then, Stop I won't! said Jipson, and Stop I won't! said Ryde.
Then stop I will! said Johnson, for I heard a woman cry.

So Johnson he alighted and viewed the place all round
And saw a naked woman with her hair pinned to the ground.

How came you here? said Johnson. How came you here? said he
Two highwaymen have a-robbed me and that you plainly see.

Then Johnson being a valiant man, a man of courage bold
He took the coat from off his back to keep her from the cold.

Then Johnson being a valiant man, a man of valiant mind
He sat her up upon his horse and mounted up behind.

And as they rode along the road as fast as they could ride
She put her fingers to her lips and gave three piercing cries.

Out sprang ten bold highwaymen with weapons in their hands
They stepped up to young Johnson and boldly bid him stand.

Then stand I will! said Johnson, as long as ever I can
For I never was in all my life afraid of any man.

And Johnson being a valiant man he made those bullets fly
Till nine of them ten highwaymen all on the ground did lie.

Now this wicked woman standing by, young Johnson did not mind
She took a knife all from his side and stabbed him from behind.

But the day it being a market day and people passing by
They saw this woman's dreadful deed and raised a hue and cry.

Then she was down to Newgate brought, bound down in irons strong
For killing the finest butcher as ever the sun shone on.

Three Jolly Huntsmen

Gardiner H1130. William Taylor, Petersfield Workhouse, Hampshire. August 1908.

It's of three jolly sportsmen went out to hunt the fox
But where shall we find him amongst the hills and rocks?

Chorus: *With my hip, hip, hip, and my holloa*
And away went the merry, merry band.
With my ran tan tan and my chivvy, chivvy chan
All over the merry, merry strand
With my ugle, ugle, ugle, went the bugle horn
Fal le ral, fal le ral, fal le ral le dee
Through the woods we'll go, brave boys
And through the woods we'll go.

The first we met was a fair maid a-combing out her locks
She swore she saw bold Reynolds amongst the farmer's ducks.

Oh the next we met was a farmer a-ploughing of his land
He swore he saw bold Reynolds amongst the ewes and lambs.

The next we met was a miller a-working of his mill
He swore he saw bold Reynolds run over yonder hill.

The next we met was a blind man as blind as he could be
He swore he saw bold Reynolds run up a hollow tree.

The next we saw was a parson and he was dressed in black
He swore he saw bold Reynolds upon the huntsman's back.

TOO MANY LOVERS

Hammond D609. Mrs R Young, Long Burton, Dorset. July 1906.

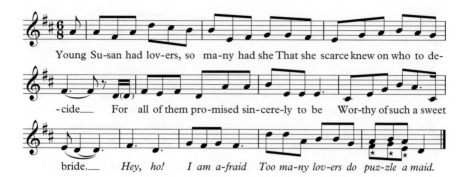

Young Susan had lovers, so many had she
That she scarce knew on who to decide
For all of them promised sincerely to be
Worthy of such a sweet bride.

Chorus: *Hey, ho! I am afraid*
            Too many lovers do puzzle a maid.

In the morning she gets up with young William to go
The noon is spent with young Harry.
In the evening with John, so amongst all the men
She doesn't know which one to marry.

Young William grew jealous and so went away
Young Harry got tired of wooing
And John, when he teased her to fix on the day
Received but a frown for so doing.

So despite all these lovers she's left in the lurch
And she pines every night on her pillow.
She met with a couple a-going to church
Turned away, and died under the willow.

THE TREADMILL SONG

Tune and text: Hammond D482. William Davy or Davey (of Hook), Beaminster
Workhouse, Dorset. June 1906.

Text: Hammond D530. Sam Gregory, Beaminster, Dorset. June 1906.

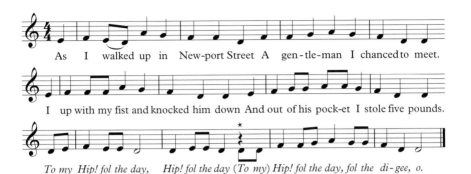

As I walked up in New-port Street A gen-tle-man I chanced to meet.

I up with my fist and knocked him down And out of his pock-et I stole five pounds.

To my Hip! fol the day, Hip! fol the day (To my) Hip! fol the day, fol the di-gee, o.

As I walked up in Newport Street
A gentleman I chanced to meet.
I up with my fist and knocked him down
And out of his pocket I stole five pounds.

Chorus: *To my Hip! fol the day, Hip!*
              fol the day
        (To my) Hip! fol the day,
              fol the digee, o.

I lay in the watch-house all last night
Till eight o'clock in the morning, o
They took me up before Mr Hook
And in his black book he did look.

Step in, young man, I know your face
'Tis nothing in your favour.
A little time I'll give to you
Six months unto hard labour.

At six o'clock our turnkey comes in
With a bunch of keys all in his hand.
Come, come, my lads, step up and grind
And tread the wheel till breakfast time.

At eight o'clock our skilly comes in
Sometimes thick and sometimes thin
And if one word we chance to say
It's bread and water all next day.

At half past eight the bell does ring.
Into the chapel we must swing
On to our bended knees must fall.
Lord have mercy on us all.

At nine o'clock the bell does ring.
All on the trap, boys, we must spring.
Come pray, my lads, to be in time
The wheel to tread and the corn to grind.

At ten o'clock the doctor comes round
With a pen and paper in his hand
And if we say we are not ill
It's all next day to the treading mill.

Now six long months is gone and past
And I'll return to my bonny lass.
I'll leave Mr Dukis here behind
His wheel to tread and his corn to grind.

THE TROOPER'S HORSE

Gardiner H783. Mrs Goodyear, Axford, Basingstoke, Hampshire. August 1907.

There was an old woman lived under the hill
   With my rowdy dowdy dow, with my rowdy dowdy day
And if she isn't gone she lives there still.
   Ah ha ha, was it so, was it so?

A jolly dragoon came riding by
He called for a pot because he was dry.

He drinkèd him up and called for another
He kissed the daughter fair, likewise the old mother.

The night coming on, the day being spent
They both went to bed with their mother's consent.

Oh what is this here so stiff and warm?
'Tis only my nag, he'll do you no harm.

But what is this? 'Tis a little well
Where your fine nag may drink his fill.

But what if my bonny nag should chance to fall in?
He must hang on the grass that grows round the brim.

But what if the grass should prove to be rotten?
He must bob up and down till he comes to the bottom.

THE TURTLE DOVE

Tune and text: Hammond D595. Edith Sartin, Corscombe, Dorset. July 1906.

Text: Hammond D841. Mr J Bridle, Stratton, Dorset. August 1907.

Text: Hammond D758. Marina Russell, Upwey, Dorset. February 1907.

Now fare you well, my own true-love I must leave you_ for_ a while But I'll re-turn to you a-gain If I go ten thou-sand miles, my dear If I go ten thou-sand miles.

Now fare you well, my own true-love
I must leave you for a while
But I'll return to you again
If I go ten thousand miles, my dear
If I go ten thousand miles.

Ten thousand miles is a very long way
But from you I must go
Where there's many a dark and a dismal night
And the stormy winds do blow, my dear
And the stormy winds do blow.

Ten thousand miles is a very long way
Through France, Scotland and Spain
She said, My heart will never be at rest
Till I see your face again, my dear
Till I see your face again.

Oh don't you see that pretty turtle dove
Sitting in yonder tree?
A-waiting for his own true-love
As I will wait for thee, my dear
As I will wait for thee.

For I am like a turtle dove
That flies from tree to tree
And as he waiteth for his mate
So I will wait for thee, my dear
So I will wait for thee.

When you see this remember me
And bear it in your mind
And be not like the weathercock
That changes with the weather and wind, my dear
That changes with the weather and wind.

THE UNFORTUNATE TAILOR

Tune and text: Gardiner H407. George Lovett, Winchester, Hampshire. August 1906.
Text: Gardiner H933. Alfred Oliver, Basingstoke, Hampshire. September 1907.

Oh list, oh list to my sorrowful lay
Attention give to my song, I pray
And when you've heard it all
    you'll say
That I'm an unfortunate tailor.

I once was as happy as a bird on
    a tree
My Sarah was all in the world to me
Now I'm cut out by a son of the sea
And she's left me here to bewail her.

Oh why did my Sarah serve me so?
No more will I stitch, no more will I sew
My thimble and my needle to the winds
    I'll throw
And go and 'list for a sailor.

My Sarah was the daughter of a publican
A generous, kind, good sort of a man
Who spoke very plain what he thought of
    a man
And he never looked crow at the tailor.

My days were honey, the nights the same
Till a man named Cobb from the
    ocean came
With his long black beard and his
    muscular frame
A captain on board of a whaler.

He spent his money both frank and free
With his tales of the land and songs of
    the sea
He stole my Sarah's heart from me
And blighted the hopes of a tailor.

When telling my love, in came that Cobb.
Avast! he cried, you lubberly swab
If you don't knock off I'll scuttle
    your knob!
And Sarah smiled at the sailor.

And now I'll cross the raging sea
Since Sarah is untrue to me
My heart's locked up and she's the key
What a very unfeeling gaoler.

So now, kind friends, I'll bid adieu
No more my woes shall trouble you.
I'll travel the country through and through
And go and 'list for a sailor.

THE UNQUIET GRAVE

Hammond D483. Jane Hann, Stoke Abbott, Dorset. June 1906.

How plea-sant is the wind to-night I feel some drops of rain
I ne-ver had but one true-love And in green-wood he was slain.
I'll do so much for my true-love As a-ny young man may
I'll sit and mourn all on his grave For a twelve-month and one day.

How pleasant is the wind tonight
I feel some drops of rain
I never had but one true-love
And in greenwood he was slain.

I'll do so much for my true-love
As any young man may
I'll sit and mourn all on his grave
For a twelvemonth and one day.

The twelvemonth and one day being up
The ghost began to speak.
Why sit you here and mourn for me
And will not let me sleep?

What do you want of me, sweetheart
Or what is it you crave?
I want one kiss of your lily-white lips
And that is all I crave.

My lips they are as cold as clay
My breath be heavy and strong.
You have one kiss of my lily-white lips
Your life will not be long.

My life be't long or short, sweetheart
But that is all I crave
Then I shall be along with you
A-lying in my grave.

'Twas down in Cupid's Garden
Where you and I would walk
The finest flower that ever was there
Is withered to a stalk.

Is withered to a stalk, sweetheart
The flower will never return
And since I lost my own sweetheart
What can I do but mourn?

Oh don't you see the fire, sweetheart
The fire that burns so blue?
Where my poor soul tormented is
While I stay here with you.

And if you wasn't my own sweetheart
As I know well you be
I'd rend you up in pieces small
As leaves upon the tree.

Mourn not for me, my dearest dear
Mourn not for me, I crave
I must leave you and all the world
And turn into my grave.

(♮) *Hammond noted, 'The B never*
flattened.'

111

THE UPS AND DOWNS

Gardiner H1134. Mr E Frankham, Petersfield, Hampshire. August 1908.

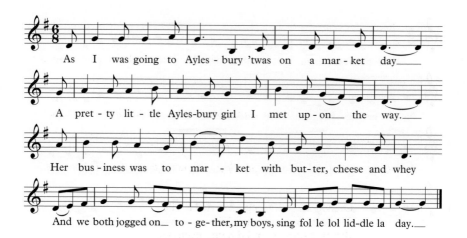

As I was going to Aylesbury 'twas on a market day
A pretty little Aylesbury girl I met upon the way.
Her business was to market with butter, cheese and whey
And we both jogged on together, my boys, sing fol le lol liddle la day.

And as we jogged on together, my boys, so happy side by side
By chance this fair maid's garter, by chance it came untied
And as we jogged on together, my boys, I unto her did say
Oh your garter's come untied, my love, sing fol le lol liddle la day.

And as we jogged on together, my boys, to the outskirts of the town
At length this fair young damsel she stopped and looked all round
Saying, Since you've been so venturesome, pray tie it up for me.
Oh I will if you'll go to yonder green grove, all under a shady tree.

And when we got to yonder green grove the grass was growing high
We both sat down together, my boys, her garter for to tie.
Such a tying of a garter the likes I never did see
We both rolled down together, my boys, sing fol le lol liddle la dee.

Now since you've had your will of me pray tell to me your name
Likewise your occupation, from where and whence you came.
My name is Mickie the drover boy, from Dublin Town I came
And I live at the sign of the Ups and Downs, sing fol le lol liddle la day.

And when she got to Aylesbury her butter had not been sold
And the losing of her maidenhead it made her blood run cold.
But now he's gone, so let him go for he's not the lad for me
For he lives at the sign of the Ups and Downs, sing fol le lol liddle la day.

A WEEK'S WORK WELL DONE

Gardiner H594. Alfred Porter, Basingstoke, Hampshire. September 1906.

On Mon-day morn-ing I mar-ried a wife Think-ing to live a so-ber life

But as it turned out I'd bet-ter been dead Than rue the day that I got wed.

Lad-dy i o! Fad-dy i o! Sing fal re lal lal lal lad-dy i o!

On Monday morning I married a wife
Thinking to live a sober life
But as it turned out I'd better been dead
Than rue the day that I got wed.

Chorus: *Laddy i o! Faddy i o!*
Sing fal re lal lal lal laddy i o!

On Tuesday morning I went to the wood
Thinking to do my wife some good
I cut a twig of holly so green
The roughest and toughest that ever was seen.

On Wednesday morning I put it to dry
On Thursday morning I gave it a try
I walloped her back and I walloped her wig
Until I broke my holly twig.

On Friday morning to my surprise
A little before the sun did rise
She opened her clatter and scolded more
Than ever I'd heard in my life before.

On Saturday morning she began again
So I beat her again very much the same
And the Devil came in in the midst of the game
And stole her away both blind and lame.

On Sunday morning I dined without
A scolding wife or a bawling bout.
I could enjoy my bottle and friend
And have a fresh wife at the week's work's end.

WILL THE WEAVER

Gardiner H920. Daniel Newman, Axford, Basingstoke, Hampshire. September 1907.

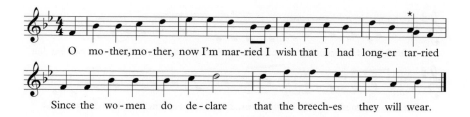

O mo-ther, mo-ther, now I'm mar-ried I wish that I had long-er tar-ried
Since the wo-men do de-clare that the breech-es they will wear.

O mother, mother, now I'm married
I wish that I had longer tarried
Since the women do declare
That the breeches they will wear.

O loving son, what is the matter?
Do she frown or do she chatter
Or do she out of season run?
What is it, my loving son?

You go home and kindly love her
Then perhaps she may recover
Give unto thy wife her due
And let me hear no more of you.

Down the street a neighbour met him
Told him something for to vex him.
The neighbour cried, I tell you true
Who was with your wife just now.

I saw her with Will the weaver
Very free and close together
At the threshold of your door
They went in, I saw no more.

He went home all in a wonder
Knocking at the door like thunder.
Who is that? the weaver cried.
'Tis my husband, you must hide.

Then she came down to let him in
Kissed her husband very prim.
Then her husband he replied
Fetch some beer for I am dry.

While she went to fetch the beer
Then he thought the house was clear
Searched the house and rooms all round
But nobody could be found.

Up the chimney chance to gazing
There he stood like one amazing
For there he saw the wretched soul
Perched upon the cotterel pole.

Oh you rogue, I'm glad I've found thee
I won't hang or I won't drown thee
But I'll stifle you with smoke.
This he thought but nothing spoke.

So he made up a rousing fire
Just to please his heart's desire.
His wife cries out with a free goodwill
Husband! There's a man you'll kill.

As he stood heaping on the fuel
Then she says, My dearest jewel
Since I am your lawful wife
Take him down and spare his life.

Then off the cotterel pole he took him
And so merrily he shook him
Every shake he gave a stroke
Saying, Come no more to stop my smoke.

Running down the street the people met him
Running as if the Devil would catch him.
Where have you been? the people cried.
Among the bacon, he replied.

Did you ever see a chimney sweeper
Half as black as Will the weaver?
A ragged coat and hat likewise
A bloody nose and two black eyes.

THE WONDERFUL SUCKING PIG

Gardiner H699. Alfred Stride, Dibden, Southampton, Hampshire. June 1907.

You all have heard of the Christmas Goose and the wal-lop-ing Great Pie
But I think to my-self it's not much use to tell such a pre-cious lie
But I will tell you a won-der now all true as I'm a sin-ner
A-bout a won-der-ful suck-ing pig we had for Christ-mas din-ner.
Tol lol le rol lol, tol lol le rol lol, tol lol le rol li day
Tol re lol re lol lol lol, tol lol le rol li day.

You all have heard of the Christmas Goose and the walloping Great Pie
But I think to myself it's not much use to tell such a precious lie
But I will tell you a wonder now all true as I'm a sinner
About a wonderful sucking pig we had for Christmas dinner.

Chorus: *Tol lol le rol lol, tol lol le rol lol, tol lol le rol li day*
           Tol re lol re lol lol lol, tol lol le rol li day.

The very first day this pig was born he cut some running capers
For he swallowed a field of turnip tops and forty tons of taters.
They took and drawed out all his teeth but it only made him snarly
For he bolted a wagon-load of swedes and a stack of oats and barley.

This sucking pig he got so fat you might think it a lark
They say his head when three weeks old was as large as Noah's ark.
One leg was as big as a greasy pole and a ton of bristles on it
And his curly tail when pulled out straight was longer than a comet.

To kill this wonderful sucking pig the folks got tired of trying
And without telling one word of a lie he was seventy years a-dying.
Two hundred men then set to work with lots of knives and choppers
And it took them all about seven years to cut off one of his trotters.

These men had one leg for their lunch so to Hyde Park they took it
And they had to boil the Sepentine before that they could cook it.
His bones were sent off to the mill to be ground up for flour
And they filled about ten thousand sacks in less than half an hour.

To see this wonderful sucking pig the people came in clusters
And the bakers bought the sacks of flour for to make Quartern Busters.
Perhaps you might think it's not all true, but I don't care a fig
For everything I've said is true about this wonderful pig.

YOUNG EMMA

Hammond D182. Joseph Elliott, Todber, Dorset. September 1905.

Mr Elliott sang (a) F-E (b) C-A-F

Young Emma was a serving girl
And she loved her sailor bold
Who ploughed the main much gold for to gain
Who ploughed the main much gold for to gain
Which long years I've been told.

Her father kept a public house
All down by the side of the sea.
Says young Emma, You can enter in
Says young Emma, You can enter in
And there this night to be.

I'll meet you in the morning
But don't let my parents know
That your name it is young Edwin
That your name it is young Edwin
That ploughs the lowlands low.

Young Edwin he sat drinking
Till 'twas time to go to bed
And little did young Edwin think
And little did young Edwin think
What sorrow came round his head.

Young Edwin he did go to bed
And he scarcely was asleep
When Emma's cruel parents
When Emma's cruel parents
To his bedroom they did creep.

They stabbed him, they dragged him
            out of bed
And to the beach did go
They sent his body sinking
They sent his body sinking
All in the lowlands low.

Young Emma she lay dreaming
She dreamed a frightful dream
She dreamed her love sat weeping
She dreamed her love sat weeping
All by a bloody stream.

'Twas early in the morning
To her father's house did go
Thinking to meet young Edwin
Thinking to meet young Edwin
That ploughed the lowlands low.

O father, where's that young man
Came here last night to stay?
He's dead, he's gone, no tales can tell
He's dead, he's gone, no tales can tell
Her father he did say.

O father, cruel father
You shall die a public show
For the murdering of my Edwin
For the murdering of my Edwin
That ploughed the lowlands low.

Then many a day she passed away
Crying to ease her mind.
Oh now, she cried, my love is gone
Oh now, she cried, my love is gone
And I am left behind.

The shells all of the ocean
Shall roll over my love's breast
For his body do lie mouldering
For his body do lie mouldering
And I hope his soul's at rest.

Then she went ranting crazy
To Bedlam forced to go
Because she loved him dearly
Because she loved him dearly
That ploughed the lowlands low.

THE YOUNG SAILOR CUT DOWN IN HIS PRIME

Hammond D349. William Curtis, Lyme Regis, Dorset. March 1906.

One day as I strolled down by the Royal Albion
Dark was the morning, cold was the day
Then who should I spy but one of my shipmates
Draped in a blanket far colder than clay.

He called for a candle to light him to bed
Likewise an old flannel to wrap round his head.
His poor head was aching, his poor heart was breaking
For he was a young sailor cut down in his prime.

Chorus: *We'll beat the drums loudly and play the pipes merrily*
                  Play the dead march as we carry him along
                  Take him to a churchyard and fire three volleys over him
                  For he's a young sailor cut down in his prime.★

His poor aged father, his good old mother
Oft-times had told him about his past life
Along with the flash girls his money he squandered
Along with those flash girls he took his delight.

But now he is dead and laid in his coffin
Six jolly sailor lads march on each side
And each of them carries a bunch of white roses
That no one might smell him as we pass 'em by.

At the corner of the street there's two girls standing
Each to the other does whisper and say
Here comes a young fellow whose money we squandered
Here comes a young sailor cut down in his prime.

On top of his tombstone these words they are written
All you young fellows take a warning by me
And never go courting those girls of the city
For those girls of the city were the ruin of me.

Mr Curtis sang the chorus after verses 2, 3, 4 and 5.

NOTES ON THE SONGS

THE brief notes printed in the original *Marrow Bones* had not been intended for publication, so for this revised edition we have prepared entirely fresh ones. A great deal of new information and analysis has become available since 1965 and, particularly with the recent rapid increase in internet-based resources, more is appearing all the time. We have incorporated as much as we can here, gleaned from our own investigations and those of others. We hope that there will be matter of interest not only to singers - at whom these books were, and are, principally aimed – but also to students on a more academic level. Our intention has been to provide the background that Frank Purslow would have supplied had he been given the opportunity when he prepared the original book, and had he had access to the resources, scarcely dreamed of in the 1960s, that are available to us today.

For several years now it has been standard practice to include 'Roud' numbers in folk song collections. Since their inception, Steve Roud's ever-expanding Folk Song and Broadside Indexes have been an invaluable tool for researchers at all levels, but until recently they were available only to subscribers and via subscribing institutions; now, however, the general public can access them at the website of the Vaughan Williams Memorial Library (http://library.efdss.org/) and they have truly come into their own. This frees us from the necessity of including long lists of further examples of songs in other publications, as interested readers can now locate these for themselves. Where items are not yet listed by Roud, or where they are especially relevant, we provide references; in particular to broadside examples of songs which can be seen in facsimile at the websites of the Bodleian Library, the University of Glasgow (Murray Collection), the National Library of Scotland, and the University of California (Pepys Collection, the originals of which are held at Magdalene College, Cambridge) and others. Bodleian broadsides are referred to by shelfmark or title; Pepys broadsides by volume and page number, with Roman numerals replaced by Arabic as at the California website.

We also list, though not exhaustively, examples of recordings of other versions of the songs printed here from traditional singers, where such are currently available. *Marrow Bones*, and the later books in the series, provided – as they were meant to – a rich source of material for 'revival' singers, but it is impractical to attempt to list all the arrangements that have subsequently been recorded (even those that acknowledge their sources) and readers wanting to gain an impression of how the songs may have sounded to Gardiner and the Hammonds will certainly benefit most by hearing them on the lips of singers from the old tradition. Details of record labels referred to, together with a few more, are included in the Bibliographies. After some consideration, we have not listed the important recordings issued by the late Peter Kennedy on his Folktrax label, as the current and future status of this is uncertain at the time of writing. Interested readers should consult his online catalogue.

Dr Gardiner worked with a series of musicians who noted tunes for him, and, where the information is available, we name them here. All songs from the Hammond collection in this book were noted by Robert (words) and Henry (music). Later books in the series identified the modal scale in which each song was sung; the majority here are Ionian (straightforward major), but where the scales are less usual, or ambiguous, we have given details. Comments such as 'no 7th' or 'inflexion (variation of a note by a semitone) of 4th' and so on, refer to the scale based on the fundamental note of the piece, not the mode/s. Our thanks to Paul Sartin for his invaluable help in this regard.

Abbreviated titles are used for books frequently referred to; see Bibliographies for key. References to the *Journal of the Folk-Song Society* (*FSJ*) are in the format 'volume number (issue number) date, page'; and to the *Journal of the English Folk Dance and Song Society* (*JEFDSS*) and the *Folk Music Journal* (*FMJ*) in the format 'volume number (part number) date, page'.

The Madden Collection of Broadside ballads is housed at the University of Cambridge Library. References given here are to the microfilm copy held at the Vaughan Williams Memorial Library. A useful introduction to Madden can be seen at http://microformguides. gale.com/Data/Introductions/30330FM.htm and the collection is indexed both at that site and in the Roud Broadside Index.

Finally, it should be noted that Gardiner MS numbers in the original edition mostly do not match the current numbering system, further material having subsequently been transcribed and added. All MS numbers in this revised edition have been amended accordingly.

THE ASTROLOGER

Roud 1598

Dorian mode.

This song is rare in oral tradition; beside two tunes and one text in Hammond, there are texts in Kinloch (37–39) and in Peter Buchan's unpublished MS *Secret Songs of Silence*, 70–72. Patrick Weston Joyce printed a tune, *There was an old astrologer*, set to a song of his brother's. 'I learned this spirited air in early days from my father,' he wrote, 'and I know the greater part of an English song to it; but it is not fit for publication.' It bears little resemblance to our melody. Broadside editions are rather more common, and include Stevenson of Gateshead, Mayne of Belfast, Pitts of London (several times), the Glasgow Poet's Box (1855), Sanderson of Edinburgh, and J Jennings of London. Mayne, and another without imprint, give it in thirteen couplets with a 'fol de rol' refrain, while the others print it in seven or eight double stanzas.

See, for example, Bodleian, Harding B 17(223b): Sanderson, *The Old Astrologer*; Harding B 25(85): J Jennings, *The Astrologer*; Johnson Ballads 718: J Pitts and G Jennings, *The Astrologer*; 2806 c.17(49): *The Bold Astrologer*; Harding B 26(378): *A New […] Called the London Astrologer*, and Harding B 6(21): *The London Fortune-teller*. Most versions are set in London, though one names Reading and one Liverpool.

The variation between broadside texts would suggest that at least some were taken from oral currency. Those that can be dated are mostly of the first part of the nineteenth century, but the song had been in circulation for some time before that; *The Crafty Maid Outwitted by the Old Fortune Teller* appeared in a chapbook, *The Jolly Gamester's Garland*, printed in Newcastle in *c*.1768 (British Library 11621.c.3.(91.)). It was reprinted in John Bell, *A Right Merry Book of Garlands*, Newcastle, *c*.1815.

Mr Penny began:

> Oh it's of a bolden astrolinger in London town did dwell
> He told pretty maiden's fortunes and there's none could him excel.
> *Sing tiddy fal lero whack fa la, sing tiddy fal lero dee.*

Penny's text has been amended from the garland. No tune was noted from him, so Marina Russell's was used; we have added her variant ending in this edition. She had no chorus, so this was omitted and Penny's eight stanzas combined into four to fit her four-line melody. Note that the second half of our stanza 3 and the first half of stanza 4 form a single stanza in the garland text.

THE BIRD IN THE BUSH

Roud 290

This song is fairly common in oral tradition in England, found in all the regions that have been extensively 'collected' except East Anglia. Broadsides seem to be relatively scarce. Kendrew of York (between 1801 and 1848) is probably the earliest, followed by Walker of Newcastle, Williamson of Newcastle (Bodleian, Harding B 11(3815) and others), Jackson of Birmingham (Harding B 11(3968)) – all these in the first half of the nineteenth century – and then, a little later, Birmingham of Dublin (probably the text reproduced in Pinto & Rodway 576–577).

Early folk song collectors tended to print shortened or altered texts because of the clear sexual symbolism of the song. Christie (*Traditional Ballad Airs*, vol II, 1881, 278–9) printed a tune – the only Scottish one we have for this song – set to unrelated words, and Baring-Gould (*Songs of the West*, first edition, 1889–92) printed a Devon tune to entirely new words, though the revised edition of 1905 reverted, probably at Cecil Sharp's instigation, to the text he got from Roger Hannaford (Lower Widdecombe, 1890), only slightly altered. The first unmediated oral text to be published was in Reeves, *Idiom of the People*, 208–209;

Cecil Sharp had got it from William Stokes at Chew Stoke, Somerset, in 1907 (see Roud, Upton & Taylor, *Still Growing*, London: EFDSS, 2003, 108, for Stokes' text with a tune from Mrs Truby of Oxfordshire; the very last song Sharp transcribed).

William Poole's text here is amended throughout in various minor particulars, mainly to enhance 'singability'; but some original readings may be preferable and should be noted. In verse 1, line 4, Mr Poole sang 'And her pails they came tinkling to and fro.' His final two verses ran:

Here's a health to the man and the maid
Here's a health to the jolly dragoon
For we're birds of one feather and all flock together
Let the people say little or much.

Then here's a health to the man and the maid
Here's a health to the jolly dragoon.
We've tarried all day and worked down the sun
So we'll bide here and drink down the moon.

The last is amended with reference to Robert Barratt's, which was:

God send us good malt for to brew (x2)
For as we tarry here for to drink down the sun, brave boys,
Let us tarry here and drink down the moon.

'The bird in the bush' in our verse 5 is probably borrowed from another version, Gardiner H845 (James Pike, Portsmouth, 1907) or from broadside editions; our title seems to be editorial, as the song is usually called 'Three Maidens a-Milking Did Go' or variations thereon. James Reeves thought the song seventeenth century or even earlier; we have no real evidence to support that, but part of it at least may derive from a playhouse or pleasure gardens song of the late eighteenth century. The following is quoted from 'The Songster's New Delight' (Bodleian, Harding B 6(13)):

A Play house SONG

Here's a good health to the King
And send him a prosperous reign
Over hills and high mountains
Until the sun rise again, brave boys.
Then here's to thee my boy aboon
Then here's &c.
As we've tarried all day
To drink down the sun
So we'll tarry to drink down the moon.

Most tunes found with this song, though they may differ considerably in detail, are recognisably related (even Christie's Aeolian form) and presumably derive from a single original. Versions from tradition can be heard on Veteran VTC4CD, *Down in the Fields* (Charlie Bridger, Kent) and Topic TSCD660, *Who's That at My Bed Window?* (Fred Hewett, Hampshire).

THE BOLD FISHERMAN

Roud 291 Laws O24

This popular song has given rise to some quite extravagant speculation in its time. Lucy Broadwood (*FSJ* V (19) 1915 132–135 and VII (27) 1923 36–40) argued that it was a 'vulgar and secularized transmutation of a medieval allegorical original', and pointed to perceived parallels in Gnostic and early Christian mystical literature. It is not impossible that it may descend from an earlier (unknown) ballad of an encounter between a poor girl and a rich noble in disguise, but the fact remains that we have no record of it prior to the nineteenth century, when it appeared on London broadsides by Catnach (see Bodleian, Firth b.25(113) and others) and his successors and, further north, by Jackson of Birmingham (Harding B 11(1825)) and, later, Sanderson of Edinburgh.

In contrast to Miss Broadwood's analysis, Renwick (chapter 1, 'The Bold Fisherman: Symbolism in English Traditional Folksong') suggests that, on the whole, the average country singer may not have been too concerned with Gnostic symbolism, and that the song may belong, less exotically, to the more familiar and enormously popular genre in which a lover returns unrecognised until identified by a token.

No text from Mrs Gulliver (or Gulliford) survives, so instead George Roper's, for which we have no music, is set to her tune. He sang the song in four-line stanzas without repeats; his text has been re-cast to fit. Instead of 'rowing' (which occurs in other oral versions) he sang 'roving'; broadsides, on the other hand, have 'rolling'. It may also be worth noting that in broadside editions the fisherman unties not his own 'morning gown' but the lady's; and that it is she, not the gown, who is then laid on the ground.

The Edinburgh broadside spawned one oral version in Scotland (*Greig-Duncan* 4, 248). A few versions turn up on the north-eastern seaboard of North America, but the song belongs primarily to the southern half of England, where Gardiner and the Hammonds found it several times, and Sharp noted fifteen versions. Examples from tradition can be heard on Topic TSCD512D, *The Bonny Labouring Boy* (Harry Cox, Norfolk, 1965); TSCD651, *Come Let Us Buy the Licence* (Harry Cox, 1934) and TSCD514, *A World Without Horses* (Walter Pardon, Norfolk); and on Coppersongs CD3, *Coppersongs 3: The Legacy Continues* (Copper Family, Sussex).

BOLD GENERAL WOLFE

Roud 624

Like Benbow and Nelson, General James Wolfe was a hero not only to the general public but also, more tellingly, to the men who served under him, and his death on the Plains of Abraham outside Quebec on 13 September 1759, in the hour of his victory, inspired a number of broadside songs. Some were contemporary with the event, as ours may also have been; though we don't have examples of it prior to the early nineteenth (possibly late eighteenth) century.

It was widely published by printers in London – see, among others, Bodleian, Harding B 11(830): T Birt; Harding B 16(71b): J Pitts; and Harding B 15(115b): J Disley – and in Bath (Whitford), Worcester (Harding B 25(716): J Grundy, perhaps late C18), Birmingham (Russell), Middlewich (2806 c.17(144): J Rosson); Newcastle-under-Lyme (Harding B 28(208): J Cooper), Chesterfield (Ford), Manchester (Firth c.26(23): J Cadman); Durham (G Walker), Newcastle (J Marshall), Glasgow (Robertson) and Cork (Haly).

Oral versions have often been found, chiefly in the south of England. Petrie (I, number 365) printed an Irish version of the tune, recognisably related to Sam Gregory's and versions have turned up in Ontario; though the song 'Brave Wolfe' (Roud 961, Laws A1), unrelated but based on the same events, is the one usually found in the USA and Canada. Recordings of versions from traditional singers can be heard on Musical Traditions, MTCD301–2, *A Broadside* (Bob Hart, Suffolk) and MTCD303, *Plenty of Thyme* (Cyril Poacher, Suffolk); and on Topic TSCD534, *Come Write Me Down* (Copper Family, Sussex). The tunes, though they vary considerably, are all clearly related to ours.

THE BOLD PRINCESS ROYAL

Roud 528 Laws K29

Tune noted by Balfour Gardiner. Ionian with inflexion of 4th.

At daybreak on 21 June 1798, HM packet *Princess Royal*, nine days out from Falmouth on her way to New York (other accounts say Halifax) carrying mail, was accosted and pursued by a brig which was later identified as the French privateer *Aventurier*. At 7 pm the *Aventurier* hoisted English colours and fired a shot, which the *Princess Royal* returned. After a further shot, the brig continued the pursuit. It was not until 3.30 am on 22 June that the *Aventurier* resumed its attack, this time with a broadside and musket fire. The *Princess Royal* was out-manned, with a crew of thirty-two men and boys with seventeen passengers as opposed to the *Aventurier's* 85 men and boys; and out-gunned too, with six cannon against the brig's sixteen. Nevertheless, the English ship gave a good account of herself, holding the privateer off for two hours; at the end of which time the *Aventurier* moved away, sustaining further damage to her stern. The French ship was obliged to return to Bordeaux for refitting, while the *Princess Royal* resumed her course, eventually arriving home on 31 October.

If, as seems likely, this is the event that gave rise to our song, then it is a mystery why the broadside writer has toned down the story instead of embellishing it. Perhaps the full details were not immediately available; it is otherwise hard to see why a dramatic engagement should have become merely an account of a successful escape. At one point it appears that, the cartridges for the four-pound guns having all been used, the captain's sister and her maid set to in the bread-room to make new ones.

Captain John Skinner himself was an interesting figure. Born in Perth Amboy, New Jersey in *c.*1760, he joined the loyalist side in the American Revolution, losing an arm and an eye early in the campaign. He took command of the *Princess Royal* in 1794, and in *c.*1801 transferred to Holyhead, where he had charge of the Post Office Service packet-boats on the Holyhead to Dublin run until his death in 1832, when he was washed overboard along with the ship's mate, and drowned. There is an impressive monument to him at Holyhead.

For broadside prints, see among others Bodleian, Firth c.12(63): Disley of London; Harding B 11(1063) Dalton's Public Library; Harding B 11(3220): Such of London; Harding B 11(384): Brooks of Bristol; and at the Murray Collection (Glasgow), Mu23–y4:019. Editions also appeared in Newcastle and Dundee. The date of sailing given varies from 6 January (Pitts) through 14 February to 14 August (this last a Dublin sheet without imprint, perhaps by Nugent); such inconsistencies are not at all unusual.

The song has lasted extremely well in oral tradition, being found throughout Britain, particularly in coastal counties, most especially Norfolk and Suffolk; and on the north-east seaboard of North America, particularly in Nova Scotia. It has crossed paths with other pirate songs, and can be found intermingled with 'Kelly the Pirate' (Roud 1625, Laws K32) among others. Mr Randall's tune is the one to which it is most commonly sung (in various forms), and the same melody is often found with 'The Indian Lass', *q.v.* It has a structural relationship to 'Villikins and his Dinah' (Roud 271, Laws M31B), and some singers tend to drift into that tune.

In verse 1, line 3, Mr Randall sang 'forty bright seamen', and in line 4 his 'from the westward bore we' has been replaced with the more familiar 'and so sailed we'.

Recordings from traditional singers can be heard on Veteran VT40CD, *Good Order! Traditional Singing and Music from the Eel's Foot* (Velvet Brightwell, Suffolk); Topic TSCD662, *We've Received Orders to Sail* (Harry Cox, Norfolk); Musical Traditions MTCD301–2, *A Broadside* (Bob Hart, Suffolk); Topic TSCD511, *Now is the Time for Fishing* (Sam Larner, Norfolk) and TSCD514, *A World Without Horses* (Walter Pardon, Norfolk). For more historical background, see William James, *Naval History of Great Britain*, Vol II, 1837; a transcription is currently available online at http://freepages.genealogy.rootsweb. com/~pbtyc/Naval_History/Vol_II/FP.html

THE BOLD TROOPER

Roud 311

Tune noted by Gamblin, amended by Guyer 23 March 1909. Ionian with inflexion of 4th.

Not common on broadsides, but these vary quite considerably in four main varieties, which may suggest earlier origins. Such printed a version and there were others in Glasgow and Edinburgh, plus several without imprint. The longest (thirteen stanzas), apparently from Northern Ireland, was set in Dublin. For examples, see Bodleian, Harding B 11(3458): Such and Firth c.14(202) ('The Bold Trooper'); Harding B 26(652) ('The Trooper'); and 2806 c.17(414) ('Tailor & Trooper'). In most versions, the 'trooper' is first described as a blacksmith. The general plot is a common one and the prospective cuckolder is most often a tailor. 'The Boatswain and the Tailor' (Roud 570, Laws Q8) was equally as popular; Gardiner and the Hammonds collected examples, one of which appears in *The Wanton Seed*. Another broadside song on the theme is 'The Tailor in a Hobble' or 'The Tailor and the Treacle Cask', though that has not apparently survived in tradition.

Our text is lightly edited in places; 'I don't give a pin', for example, used here for the rhyme, was sung 'I don't give a hang'. It isn't clear from the MS whether the chorus was sung the same throughout, or whether the final lines of each verse were used. Singers may choose for themselves.

Oral versions have been found in the southern counties and East Anglia; it is also reported from Scotland, Ireland, the USA and Canada (mainly Newfoundland). In 1954 or 1955, Bob Copper recorded a version from Frank Cole of North Waltham that was almost identical in words and tune to Jesse Cole's: it is transcribed in Bob's book *Songs and Southern Breezes* (London: Heinemann, 1973, 270–1). We don't know whether the two men were related, but Frank was the son-in-law of Mrs Randall of Ellifield (previously of Preston Candover), from whom Gardiner got several songs. Recordings from tradition can be heard on Topic TSCD512D, *The Bonny Labouring Boy* (Harry Cox, Norfolk) and TSCD656, *Tonight I'll Make You My Bride* (Nora Cleary, Clare).

THE BONNY BUNCH OF ROSES O!

Roud 664 Laws J5

Tune noted by Guyer. Ionian, no 7th.

The broadside presses produced a great many songs featuring Napoleon; on the whole it is those which treat him sympathetically that have survived in tradition. In Ireland he was seen as a potential liberator, and in Britain he was something of a hero to the growing Radical and Republican movements. For a useful introduction to the subject, see Vic Gammon's article 'The Grand Conversation: Napoleon and British Popular Balladry' on the *Musical Traditions* website (http://www.mustrad.org.uk/articles/boney.htm).

'The song', wrote Frank Purslow in his original notes, 'is an imaginary conversation between Napoleon's young son and his mother' [Maria Louisa of Austria] '... verse 4 is a continuance of his mother's warning, not ... a statement of unhistorical fact. When young Napoleon speaks of "The deeds of bold Napoleon" he is referring to the deeds of his father, not of himself.' François Charles Joseph Bonaparte, 'Young Napoleon', died of tuberculosis in Vienna in 1832, so our song must have been written a little after that. On a broadside issued by Hill of London (Bodleian, Harding B 15(394b)) as 'Young Napoleon, or The Bunch of Roses', the words are credited to a George Brown, about whom nothing seems to be known beyond the fact that he is also credited on various broadsides as writer of such songs as 'Flora the Lily of the West' (Roud 957, Laws P29), 'The Merchant's Daughter and Constant Farmer's Son' (Roud 675, Laws M33), and 'The Grand Conversation on Napoleon' (Roud 1189).

The song was published by most of the main broadside printers, with some textual variation; a number of examples can be seen at the Bodleian Library website as 'Young Napoleon', 'Young Napoleon or The [Bonny] Bunch of Roses', and '[The] Bonny Bunch of Roses, O'. On some, the tune 'The Bunch of Rushes, O' is prescribed; for which, see 'The Bonny Bunch of Rushes' in this book. Some oral versions use it, but Charles Windebank's tune was a different one, a variant of 'The Rose Tree'; this got its name from John O'Keefe's lyric, 'A Rose Tree in Full Bearing', which was set to it in William Shield's opera *The Poor Soldier* (1782). It was well known in various forms both as a song and a dance tune; the Bampton morris team still dance to it, while in Scotland it is known as 'Johnny's Grey Breeks' (Roud 7141). In his MS notes, Gardiner quoted a couple of lines from the latter, adding drily: 'The streets are now singing with the tune, which has been turned to base use by a singer called Harry Lauder.'

Quite widely found in tradition. Examples can be heard on Veteran VT154CD, *Good Hearted Fellows* (George Ling, Suffolk); VTD148CD, *A Shropshire Lad* (Fred Jordan, Shropshire) and VT145CD, *The Gower Nightingale* (Phil Tanner, Glamorgan); on Topic TSCD512D, *The Bonny Labouring Boy* (Harry Cox, Norfolk) and TSCD658, *A Story I'm Just About to Tell* (Cyril Poacher, Norfolk); and on Musical Traditions MTCD303, *Plenty of Thyme* (Cyril Poacher) and MTCD309–10, *Just Another Saturday Night* (Bill Porter, Sussex).

THE BONNY BUNCH OF RUSHES

Roud 831

A song seldom found in oral collections, perhaps because of its obvious sexual symbolism. It appeared on broadsides by Evans, Pitts, Catnach, Such and Hook of Brighton in a four-stanza form, while Swindells of Manchester and Armstrong of Liverpool printed longer versions including a verse not in Robert Barratt's set, but lacking his final lines. A slightly longer form was published by Coverley of Boston, Massachusetts, but the ending is different. See Bodleian, Harding B 17(42a) : Evans; Harding B 11(486): Pitts; Harding B 11(485): Such; Harding B 28(144): Armstrong; and two without imprint, Firth c.18(299) and Harding B 25(311).

The English broadside seems to have been based on an Irish-language song called 'An Beinsín Luachradh', which tells a similar story but in rather more ornate terms. Three macaronic versions of this were printed in *FSJ* III (10) 1907, 17–21, and an example from tradition (this time in English, sung by Philip McDermott, Fermanagh, as 'The Reaping of the Rushes Green') can be heard on Musical Traditions MTCD329–0, *The Hardy Sons of Dan*, and Topic TSCD668, *To Catch a Fine Buck was My Delight*. The English-language form is presently classed as Roud 3380.

The tune appears as 'An Beartín Luachra' in Edward Bunting, *A General Collection of the Ancient Music of Ireland* (II, 1809, 39); Mr Barratt's melody is recognisably related, and some versions of 'The Bonny Bunch of Roses', *q.v.*, also use forms of it. In verse 1, he sang 'strangers' rather than 'lovers', and in verse 3 his tree was 'shady' instead of 'spreading'. His final full verse ended:

So come all you gentle reeders as to those reedes you do go
Pray don't forget the answer to the new made bunch of rushes, o.

At the beginning of the final, solitary line, Barratt sang an emphatic 'Yo!' as was his usual custom.

On sexual metaphor in folk song, see Reeves, *Everlasting Circle*, Introduction, part 5, 'The *Lingua Franca*'; Renwick, chapter 2, 'The Semiotics of Sexual Liaisons'; and Barre Toelken, *Morning Dew and Roses: Nuance, Metaphor and Meaning in Folksongs* (Urbana and Chicago: University of Illinois Press, 1995).

THE BONNY LABOURING BOY

Roud 1162 Laws M14

Dorian mode.

Widely printed on broadsides by Pitts and his successors, then in Birmingham, Manchester, Hull, Newcastle, Dublin and Belfast; and finally by Sanderson of Edinburgh. The fullest versions (Hodges, for instance) have twelve stanzas, and the couple finally elope to Plymouth. For examples, see Bodleian, Johnson Ballads 311: Disley of London; Johnson Ballads 1437: Pratt of Birmingham; Firth c.18(177): Pearson of Manchester; Harding B 19(17): Nugent of Dublin; and Harding B 19(43): Birmingham of Dublin.

In verse 5, line 1, Robert Barratt sang 'Oh his cheeks is like the roses, his eyes so black as sloes'; dialectal 'is' and 'so' have been replaced with standard forms, but the originals should be noted. This verse is normally fourth in broadside copies, and might more naturally follow verse 2 here. Mr Barratt's tune belongs to the large family often referred to as 'Lazarus' from the association of one branch with the song 'Dives and Lazarus' (Roud 47, Child 56), and other versions of 'The Bonny Labouring Boy' are also sung to forms of it, though they can vary widely in detail and modal form. Several other songs in this book also have related melodies, some more obviously so than others. For more on the group and its history, see Simpson, 252–4 ('Gilderoy') and 109 ('The Clean Contrary Way').

Oral versions have been found all over England and Ireland, the USA and Canada, but not in Scotland, where broadside editions were late appearing. Some examples from tradition can be heard on Veteran VTC4CD, *Down in the Fields* (Jeff Wesley, Northamptonshire); Topic TSCD512D, *The Bonny Labouring Boy* (Harry Cox, Norfolk) and TSCD655, *Come My Lads that Follow the Plough* (Paddy Beades, Dublin); and Musical Traditions MTCD331, *The Birds Upon the Tree* (Bob Blake, Sussex).

THE BOYS OF KILKENNY

Roud 1451

Aeolian mode.

At the beginning of the nineteenth century, Michael Kelly of 9, Pall Mall printed a songsheet with music, 'The Boys of Kilkenny, A Favorite Irish song' dedicated to a Colonel Doyle. Whether or not Kelly was responsible for putting the song into that form and localising it to Kilkenny is uncertain; at around the same time, other printers issued a song, 'The Riddle', which mixed 'Kilkenny' verses with 'I will give my love an apple' riddle stanzas (Roud 330) also associated with 'Captain Wedderburn's Courtship' (Roud 36 Child 46); see Bodleian, Harding B 25(1620) for an example by Jennings of London; there were others by Pitts and Taylor.

'Boys of Kilkenny' was also printed in five-stanza versions by Pitts, Catnach and Batchelar in London and Williams of Portsea, but later London printers only used the first four of these, and were largely followed in this by provincial printers in Birmingham, Manchester, York, Newcastle, Glasgow and Edinburgh. The broadsides show little variety. See, among others, Bodleian, Harding B 11(2403): Pitts; 2806 b.11(241): Such; 2806 b.11(171): Stewart of Carlisle; Firth b.34(212): Ordoyno of Nottingham. See the Levy Collection for examples of sheet music of *c.*1835 set to the Irish 'Old Head of Denis' tune that Kelly used. 'The True Lovers Farewell' (Harding B 25(1953)) also uses some of the same material.

The song has a wide range of close relatives that feature other place names from all over the British Isles (Sunderland, Udny, Portmore, Paisley and others) and the family has various ancestors dating back at least to the seventeenth century. See in particular 'Shrowsbury for Me' (Pepys 2.135 and Bodleian, 4o Rawl. 566(26), Douce Ballads 2(206a) and Wood E 25(44)), which has stanzas in common with the much later 'Kilkenny' redaction.

Other related songs are listed in Roud, and there is also an overlap with 'The Streams of Lovely Nancy' (Roud 688). The whole extended family would merit further investigation; for some commentary and broadside texts, see the late Bruce Olson's website (http://www. csufresno.edu/folklore/Olson/SONGTXT1.HTM#BYSKLKN).

Jim Burrows' song seems to have been a 'Riddle' derivative (Roud 330) rather than a mainstream 'Kilkenny' variant; he began:

> As I was a-walking one morning in June
> Down by some pleasant riverside by myself all alone

followed by lines 3 and 4 of our verse 2. He then sang our verse 3, followed by four 'riddle' verses. Our verse 1 is from T Hunt (though he sang 'Fare you well to old England'); his other verse was almost the same as Mr Burrows'. Verses 4 and 5 are from elsewhere; probably adapted from standard 'Kilkenny' broadsides. The tune bears no particular resemblance to 'Denis' or its relatives. Oral versions are scarce, and we know of no recordings from tradition.

THE BREWER LADDIE

Roud 867

Ionian, no 4th.

This Scottish broadside ballad appears to have strayed a long way from home. It seems to be the only substantial version found south of the Tees; Frank Kidson printed a tune from Westmoreland, Cecil Sharp collected a fragment in Somerset and Gardiner got a fragment in Wiltshire, but all other oral versions come from Scotland where the action is firmly set in Perth and the rival lover is from Edinburgh. Identical twelve-stanza broadsides were printed in Glasgow, Edinburgh, Newcastle and Durham in the early nineteenth century under the same title given here. For the edition from Fordyce of Newcastle, see Bodleian, 2806 c.11(234).

Mrs Bowditch's title was 'In Bilberry Town'. 'Is this meant for Milbury, of which there are two in Dorset?' wondered Hammond. A localisation seems likely enough; the one-stanza version Sharp found began 'In Dover Town'. Kidson (86–8) printed a Glasgow chapbook text with his Westmoreland tune, so we don't know if there was also a localisation there.

Mrs Bowditch's tune is very close to Kidson's; rather less so to Scottish versions of 'The Brewer Laddie', though Jeannie Robertson's tune for 'She Was a Rum One' (Roud 2128), a simple account of a sexual encounter, is a very near relative and has virtually the same chorus. It can be heard on Rounder ROUN1720, *Jeannie Robertson: The Queen Among the Heather.*

THE BRICKLAYER'S DREAM

Roud 971

Tune noted by Gamblin.

Scarce on broadsides and in oral tradition, this four-stanza ballad seems to have a lowland version called 'The Bricklayer's Dream' printed by John Forth of Pocklington, East Yorks, and his brother, William of Hull; and an upland version called 'The Stonecutter Bold' printed by Ford of Sheffield. They don't vary much textually. Oral versions of the former have been found in Hampshire (this version), Sussex (George Townshend and 'Brick' Harber, though Harber was of Worcestershire stock and, his family being in the brickmaking trade, may have got it from them) and Gloucestershire (Hammond G314); and of the latter in Somerset (Henry Thomas and William Stokes, both noted by Sharp). Considering that we have only broadsides from Yorkshire and oral versions from southern

England, one must surmise that other broadside versions once existed that have not survived.

We have only one verse, the first, from Daniel Wigg; the rest is adapted from Hammond G314 ('The Brickster Boy', from an unnamed singer in – probably – Gloucestershire, with no tune noted) with modifications from 'Brick' Harber's version, which was sung to a related melody.

For an unidentified broadside, see Bodleian, Harding B 11(446): 'The Bricklayer Bold'. Examples from tradition can be heard on Musical Traditions MTCD309–10, *Just Another Saturday Night: Sussex 1960* ('Brick' Harber) and MTCD304, *Come Hand to Me the Glass* (George Townshend; one verse only). A wax cylinder recording that is probably Daniel Wigg singing 'Lord Nelson' can be heard at the website of *English Dance and Song*, the magazine of EFDSS (http://www.eds.efdss.org/) and at the British Library's *Collect Britain* website (http://www.collectbritain.co.uk/): EFDSS Cylinder No.95.

THE BRISK YOUNG BUTCHER

Roud 167

Published by all of the major English broadside printers of the nineteenth century, mostly as 'The Leicestershire Chambermaid'. The butcher is usually from London and the maid from Leicestershire, as here, but some of the Manchester broadsides localise the story to Manchester. The Greig-Duncan collection has 15 versions, mostly relocated to Aberdeenshire, while John Ord's (*Bothy Songs and Ballads*, 1930, 158; repr Edinburgh: John Donald, 1995) is set in Morpeth. Beside a couple of examples from North Yorkshire and Cumberland, there are a good few southern versions in the MSS of Sharp, Hammond and Gardiner, and a single set from Quebec.

The Pitts broadside is the earliest we know of. See Bodleian, Harding B 11(2654): Pitts; Johnson Ballads 216: Catnach; Firth c.18(304): Batchelar; Firth b.28(25a): Watts of Birmingham; Harding B 11(2104): Bebbington of Manchester; and Harding B 11(2103): Harkness of Preston. Evans of Chester issued the song as 'The Chambermaid' (2806 c.17(68)) and there is a Scottish edition in the Murray Collection at Glasgow University Library (mu23–y1:040) titled 'The Butcher and the Chamber Maid'. There are other songs founded on the same basic joke, one such being 'Change for a Guinea, or the Christmas Goose' (Roud 3204): see Bodleian, Firth c.26(157).

Alfred Scannell's text is slightly amended here. It contained no repeats, and these are added to fit George Hatherill's tune, for which no text was recorded. Verse 3, line 2, was missing; this has been replaced from a broadside. Mr Scannell had an additional verse, which fits between our stanzas 5 and 6:

> The landlady then called the maid and charged her with the same
> One sovereign she did lay down fearing to get the blame.
> The butcher he went home well pleased with what was past
> And soon the buxom chambermaid got thick about the waist.

A traditional example can be heard on Topic TSCD660, *Who's That at My Bed Window?* (Harvey Nicholson, Cumberland: 'The Copshawholme Butcher').

THE CAPTAIN'S APPRENTICE

Roud 835

Dorian, no 6th.

There is broadside with no imprint, entitled 'A New Copy of Verses: Made on Captain Mills, now under Confinement in Newgate at Bristol, for the murder of Thomas Brown his Apprentice Boy.' The sole copy known is in the St Bride's Foundation Library and was discovered there by Mike Yates; on stylistic grounds, Roy Palmer dates it to c.1800. This bears an extraordinary resemblance to an earlier ballad known as 'Captain James' (also Roud 835) which stems from an American broadside; the ballad is only found in that form in North America. Many of the details described match up with details in the 'Captain Mills' story.

Oral versions have been found in Dorset, Somerset and Norfolk. No less extraordinary is the striking similarity to another incident which happened in 1857 around King's Lynn; in that case the captain's name was Doyle and his victim was Robert Eastick, aged 15. Elizabeth James examines the subject in '*The Captain's Apprentice* and the Death of Young Robert Eastick of King's Lynn: a Study in the Development of a Folk Song' (*FMJ* 7, number 5, 1999, 579–594). She suggests that the ballad's popularity in Norfolk may have been due to history repeating itself in this way; not least because Lynn had a St James' workhouse. Events of the kind were not rare, and similar stories can be found in other seaports around the country. In 1881 William Papper, apprenticed aboard a Hull fishing smack, was cruelly mistreated and murdered in much the same way and this was also printed in verse form on a broadside; another example was the similar murder of Andrew (or John) Ross (or Rose) in 1857 ('Andrew Rose', Roud 623).

Edith Sartin only remembered the final verse; our stanzas 1, 2 and 3 (amended in places; 'hard arbour', for instance, is changed to 'yard-arm') are from George House, while 4 and 5 are adapted from Harry Cox's version, which can be heard, as 'Come all You Men throughout this Nation' on Topic TSCD662, *We've Received Orders to Sail*. His tune bears no resemblance to Mrs Sartin's, which however does seem distantly related to the 'wild … remarkable' tune that Vaughan Williams got from James Carter of King's Lynn in 1905; and, indeed, to a 'Captain James' melody found by Helen Creighton in Canada in 1954.

A CHILD'S CALENDAR

Roud 1599

Tune noted by Gamblin.

These verses were written – apparently for her own children – by Sara Coleridge (1802–52), daughter of the poet Samuel Taylor Coleridge. They appeared in her book *Pretty Lessons in Verse, for Good Children* (1834), which was reprinted from time to time until at least 1927; occasionally they still turn up in anthologies of children's verse. Samuel Gray was 42 when Gamblin noted the song from him; his text was very close to the original, which he may well have learned at school, perhaps directly from the book. Whether the tune was his own or not we can't tell; it doesn't seem to have been recorded by any other collectors. Evidently the poem persisted in the nursery for a good while; Michael Flanders and Donald Swann's parody, 'A Song of the Weather', appeared in Joyce Grenfell's show *Joyce Grenfell Requests the Pleasure* (1954) and in their own revue *At the Drop of a Hat* (1956).

COLIN'S GHOST

Roud 1600

Ionian with inflexions of 4th and 7th.

Only verses 1 and 3 are from Mrs Webb; she sang 'hobble and trot'. The rest is added from a broadside by Pitts, for which see Bodleian, Firth c.18(76) and Harding B 25(395); note, however, that our heroine had ale for her supper rather than tea. It was also issued by J Evans and by J Jennings. Gardiner got sets from Moses Mills and David Marlow; the song is otherwise unrecorded in tradition. Holloway and Black, I, 65–6, print the Evans text, commenting, 'Probably a concert piece'.

THE COMFORT OF MAN

Roud 1601

Tune noted by Gamblin. Ionian, no 7th. F♯ indication in the key signature removed, as that note does not occur in the tune.

The Hammond (Henry Adams) and Gardiner (George Digweed) examples are the only oral versions we know of. For broadside editions, see Bodleian, Firth c.20(140): Pitts; Firth c.20(141): Catnach; Firth b.25(229): Forth of Bridlington; Harding B 20(61): Harkness of Preston; and Harding B 11(1067): Fordyce of Newcastle. The song was also issued by Lindsay of Glasgow (see the National Library of Scotland's *Word on the Street* website at http://www.nls.uk/broadsides/) and in Dublin.

The text here is mostly George Digweed's, with amendments from Henry Adams. Verse 5 is from Adams, while verse 4, lines 3–4, and verses 7 and 9 are adapted from broadside copies. Mr Digweed had a final verse not included here:

Now all you young men as are going to be wed
Don't you be catched like a bird with a small piece of bread.
When you are catched you're a member for life
I would have you be careful in choosing a wife.

This, and our verse 8, actually come from a different song, 'Be Careful in Choosing a Wife' (Roud 4744) which was widely printed on broadsides but is almost unheard of in tradition; though Edith Sartin (Hammond D597) knew it. Mr Digweed's tune is a form of 'Richard of Taunton Dean' or 'Dumble Dum Deary' (Roud 382), to which many nineteenth-century comic songs were set.

THE CROCKERY WARE

Roud 1490

Tune noted by Gamblin.

A song from the repertoire of William (Billy) J Ashcroft (1845–1918). Ashcroft was a popular singer, comedian and dancer; he was proprietor of the Royal Alhambra Theatre of Varieties, Belfast, from 1879 to 1900. For a broadside edition, see Bodleian, Harding B 28(37). Oral versions have turned up in the north of Ireland, the southern half of England, and Canada; with the location given variously as Bristol, Limerick, Lincolnshire, London, Swansea and Worcester.

The text here is a collation made from Isaac and Charles Hobbes' versions (Charles had 'Belfry town', presumably a corruption of 'Belfast town') and from a ballad sheet in the British Library, probably with touches from other oral examples. The first part of our tune bears a strong resemblance to 'The Rose Tree'; this is less marked in other versions, though they all seem to be related in some degree. A traditional set can be heard on Veteran VT134CD, *Linkin' o'er the Lea* (Maggie Murphy, Fermanagh).

COMPLIMENTS RETURNED

Roud 1602

Tune noted by C S Parsonson.

Apparently a product, as 'I Don't Think Much of You', of the early music hall or its predecessors. For various broadside issues, with quite widely varying texts, see Bodleian, Johnson Ballads 1841: Barr of Leeds, c.1840; Firth b.26(385): J Scott of Pittenweem and J Wood of Edinburgh; Firth b.25(396): Hodges of London, between 1846 and 1854; and Harding B 18(269): H De Marsan of New York, c.1860. It was sufficiently well known to be named in Stephen C Foster's 'catalogue' song 'The Song of All Songs' (1863).

Apart from Thomas Bennet's version, there are three Aberdeenshire examples in the Greig-Duncan collection; other than that, it seems not to have been recorded by collectors. Gardiner remarked: 'words and melody seem poor and modern'. Mr Bennet's text is closest to the Edinburgh broadside. In verse 6 he sang 'but now I think I'll cut my chap'; this was amended here to 'shut my trap', which makes better sense in the immediate context; but the broadside reading is 'cut my chaff'.

THE CROCODILE

Roud 886

Tune noted by Guyer.

Issued by Catnach and Pitts and a range of printers across Britain, up to the Glasgow Poet's Box (1852), and likely a product, *c.*1830, of the London 'supper rooms' that preceded the music hall of the 1850s. The song belongs to a genre that students of folk song have tended to describe as 'songs of lies and marvels' and which tell of a wonderful event ('The Great Meat Pie') or animal ('The Sucking Pig', *q.v.*). nineteenth-century examples often refer to each other; 'The Great Meat Pie', for example, begins 'You've heard of the wond'rous crocodile', and the Glasgow Poet's Box edition specified the 'Crocodile' tune for it. Songs like 'The Derby Ram' (Roud 126) are likely to have been an influence. For broadsides, see Bodleian, Harding B 11(4288): Pitts; Harding B 11(1317): Such; 2806 c.16*(150): Jacques of Manchester; Harding B 11(4290): Walker of Durham; Firth c.19(250): Glasgow Poet's Box; and others without imprint.

Henry Lee's verse 3 is a conflation of two broadside verses:

This crocodile I could plainly see
Was not of the common race
For I was obliged to climb up a very high tree
Before I could see his face.
And when he lifted up his jaw
Tho' perhaps you'll think it was a lie
It reached above the clouds for miles three score
And his nose nearly touched the sky.

Whilst up aloft and the stream was high
It blew a gale from the south (*etc.*)

Mr Lee sang 'steam as high'; 'stem' here seems to be an error made by Gardiner's copyist, though given the compacted nature of the verse it makes better sense. In verse 1 he sang 'per orse', perhaps not being familiar with 'perforce'. The tune noted by Guyer is really just a 'snapshot' of Lee's singing; the MS includes the comment 'innumerable variants'. An example from tradition can be heard on Rounder ROUN1839, *What Will Become of England?* (Harry Cox, Norfolk). The tune there is very close to 'The Sucking Pig' in this book.

THE CROPPY BOY

Roud 1030 Laws J14

Tune noted by Gamblin. Mixolydian/Ionian with inflexion of 7th.

Evidently an Irish song, though Irish broadside editions are relatively late. The earliest English copies are from Pitts and Catnach, followed by many others. Some have twelve stanzas, but most either follow Pitts (ten) or Catnach (nine). The twelve-stanza versions are not the earliest and may have had verses added, though not always the same ones. The broadsides vary enough to suggest the ballad was already in oral tradition by the time Pitts and Catnach came to print it. Although Lord Cornwall appears in most versions, he is Lord Colonel Wall in one, and in the Pitts version he is Lord Cromwall (*sic*). A text from the log of the ship *Galaxy* (Salem, 1827) is quoted in Gale Huntington, *Songs the Whalemen Sang* (New York: Dover Publications, 1970, 188–190) and also shows signs of oral processing. See Bodleian, Harding B 15(73a): Catnach; Harding B 11(1486): Pitts; Harding B 11(763): Henson of Northampton; Harding B 11(1423): Keys of Devonport; 2806 b.10(50): Pratt of Birmingham; Harding B 11(746): Such; 2806 c.9(9): Haly of Cork; Harding B 40(6): Nugent of Dublin; and other copies. Two American editions can be seen at the *America Singing* website of the Library of Congress.

Joyce (62) dates the song to the Wexford insurgency of 1798. Various explanations of the term 'croppy' have been suggested; most commonly that it refers to hair cut close to indicate sympathy with the French Revolution. There may also be some connection with the old practice of cropping the ears (or merely the hair) of convicted felons; the term was also used generally in nineteenth century slang of ex-gaolbirds.

Mrs Munday, who Gardiner described as having 'a rich contralto voice' and 'a strong instinct for the beautiful in music' wrote the words out for him herself, as did several of the Axford singers. Her handwriting was large and bold, but her spelling was variable; Gardiner 'corrected' the MS. Her verse order is slightly changed here: our verse 3 actually came after verse 5. Verse 4 isn't from her version, and so far we have not placed it. Her tune has similarities to John Pomery's melody for 'The Sailor Deceived', *q.v.*, and to other versions of 'The Croppy Boy' and the 'Sailor's Life' family (Roud 273, Laws K12).

Found in oral currency in England, Ireland, the USA and Canada; though not in great quantity. Examples from tradition can be heard on Musical Traditions MTCD331–2, *Around the Hills of Clare* (Tom Lenihan, Clare) and MTCD309–10, *Just Another Saturday Night* (Ted and Bet Porter, Sussex).

The Cruel Mother

Roud 9 Child 20

Aeolian, no 6th.

The only known broadside appearance of this widespread song is a sheet issued by Jonah Deacon in London in the closing years of the seventeenth century: 'The Duke's Daughter's Cruelty: Or, The Wonderful Apparition of two Infants whom she Murther'd and Buried in a Forrest, for to hide her Shame.' A facsimile (Pepys 5.4) can be seen at the website of the University of Santa Barbara: http://emc.english.ucsb.edu/ballad_project/. Though it contains elements familiar in traditional forms such as the setting in York, the song has undergone considerable change over the years; Scottish versions in particular, and many American ones, have acquired a catalogue of penances from 'The Maid and the Palmer' (Roud 2335 Child 21); English examples tend to finish with a direct promise of hellfire. There is also a sub-group of children's game-songs, particularly popular in Ireland, where the revenant babes are replaced by policemen.

Mrs Case's version was short, and verses 1, 2, 10 and 11 here are introduced from elsewhere. We haven't so far traced 1 and 10, though similar forms occur in other versions, while 2 may be adapted from Gardiner H1128 (Richard Moore):

> She lent [sic] her back against an oak
> And there she thought that her back was broke

– perhaps further modified from verse 3 of Hammond D98 'Deep in Love', *q.v.*; though similar lines occur in other 'Cruel Mother' variants, chiefly North American ones. The closest lines to verse 11 we have found are from the set Cecil Sharp got from Mrs Woodberry, Ash Priors, Somerset, 1907:

> O yes, dear mother, we can tell
> For it's we to heaven and you to hell.

Beside its kinship with other 'Cruel Mother' tunes found in England, Scotland and America, Mrs Case's is obviously related to the melody commonly used for English forms of 'Geordie' (Roud 90 Child 209); Bronson prints her tune as his example 20.4 (Group A), and comments; 'The outlines of this typical tune can be traced, in one meter or another, in scores of folk-tunes, from "How should I your true love know?" onward to the present time. For illustrations of its keeping a recognisable identity through changes of all sorts, c.f. the above with Sharp's 5/4 version of "Searching for Lambs" [Roud 576] ... and with the Scottish tunes for "Thomas the Rhymer" [Roud 219 Child 37].'

Recordings from tradition can be heard on Elphinstone Institute EICD002, *Binnorrie* (Elizabeth Stewart, Aberdeenshire) and EICD003, *Rum Scum Scoosh* (Stanley Robertson, Aberdeenshire) 'She's Leaned Her Back'; Musical Traditions MTCD311–2, *Up in the North and Down in the South* (Vicky Whelan, Manchester) 'There was a Lady Dressed in Green' (a game-song form) and on MTCD335–6, *In Memory of Lizzie Higgins* and Topic TSCD653, *O'er His Grave the Grass Grew Green* (Lizzie Higgins, Aberdeenshire).
For more background, see:
David Atkinson, 'History, Symbol and Meaning in "The Cruel Mother"', in *FMJ* 6 (3) 1992, 359–380
Steve Gardham, 'The Duke's Daughter's Cruelty' (originally in *English Dance and Song* vol 64 part 3, autumn 2002, 15) and 'The Cruel Mother Revisited'; both online at http://www.mustrad.org.uk/articles/dungheap.htm
Annie G Gilchrist, 'Note on "The Lady Drest in Green" and Other Fragments of Tragic Ballads and Folk-Tales Preserved Amongst Children', in *FSJ* VI (22) 1919, 80–90.
Child I, 218–227. Bronson I, 276–296.

DEEP IN LOVE

Roud 18829; see also Roud 60

One of a large group of lover's laments that have been around in one form or another since at least the seventeenth century. The stanzas in this and indeed most versions have come together from different sources, as can be seen by the rhyme scheme: our stanzas 1, 2, 6, 7 and 8 have an *aabb* pattern, 3 is *abab*; while 4 and 5 are *abcb*. Although these lover's lament songs can be adapted to either-sex narration, particularly 'Deep in Love', the lamenting lover is usually female as here. The common stock of 'floating verses' amounts to about twenty and these are found in a wide variety of combinations in each version. To complicate things even further, versions of this song often overlap with other lover's laments such as 'The Brisk Young Sailor', so that in some cases it is almost impossible to say whether a particular stanza belongs to one lament or another. Occasionally several from the general stock have been thrown together to make up a broadside ballad. For example, 'The Complaining Lover' (T Wise, London, c.1780: Madden Collection (Slip Songs A–G) VWML microfilm 71, item 347) includes our stanzas 1, 2, 7 and 8; 'Picking Lilies' (c.1782, reproduced in *Everlasting Circle*, 91) and 'The Unfortunate Swain', (Bodleian, Harding B 22(312)) both have 1, 3, 4 and 5; and 'The Distressed Virgin' (1663–74, Bodleian, 4o Rawl. 566(160)) has our 4 and 5.

Jacob Baker sang two extra lines with his second verse, presumably to the second part of the tune:

Her gold will waste, her beauty blast,
And in time she'll come like me at last

These are again from the 'common stock', as is his eighth verse, omitted in the original edition:

Now if ever I gain my liberty
And that I trust it soon will be
I'll buy me a delicate gown to wear
Not stitched with sorrow nor hemmed with fear.

Mr Baker's tune is one of a group often associated with these songs, and also frequently with 'A Sailor's Life' (Roud 273 Laws K12) among others. A recording from tradition can be heard on Topic TSCD661, *My Father's the King of the Gypsies* (Jasper Smith, Surrey).

THE DEVIL AND THE FARMER'S WIFE

Roud 160 Child 278

Tune noted by Gamblin.

A widely travelled and very popular song, found in Britain, Ireland, the USA and Canada. As a folktale it is known all over the world; in this country it was turned into a broadside ballad as early as 1630, though this is not directly related to our song. ('A Pleasant New ballad, you here may behold, how the Devill, though subtle, was gul'd by a Scold'. See Bodleian, 4o Rawl. 566(169), for a later edition.) Pitts issued a broadside, 'The Sussex Farmer' (Bodleian, Harding B 25(1855)), which shows no chorus but is close to traditional versions. The song must have been circulating orally for some while before that; Burns provided a re-written copy of a Scottish version, 'Kellyburnbraes', for *The Scots Musical Museum* (IV, 1792, no. 379) and the song has often appeared in Scotland and Ireland under forms of that title. The earliest reference to the whistled part seems to be in Dixon-Bell, where a text (Ballad LXI) is printed as 'The Farmer's Old Wife: a Sussex Whistling Song':

'The tune is "Lilli Burlero", and the song is sung as follows:– the first line of each verse is given as a solo; then the tune is continued by a chorus of whistlers, who whistle that portion of the air which in "Lilli Burlero" would be sung to the words, "Lilli Burlero bullen a la". The songster then proceeds with the tune, and sings the whole of the verse through, after which the strain is resumed and concluded by the whistlers. The effect, when accompanied by the strong whistles of a group of lusty countrymen, is very striking, and cannot be adequately conveyed by description.'

Although tunes found with this song sometimes have a resemblance to 'Lillibulero', it may be that that particular version was sung to it by analogy rather than natively; Bronson (IV, number 278, 174–212) prints 71 examples with music and analyses the basic structure underlying the numerous variants. Interestingly, he cites the sixteenth-century melody 'The Carman's Whistle' as analogous, and Charles Gamblin's tune actually bears a strong resemblance to it.

Gamblin's text appears to have been lost; it is not transcribed in the Gardiner MSS and we have not so far established the source of the text printed here. Other examples in Hammond and Gardiner correspond to it in places, but none really match. Recordings made from tradition can be heard on Musical Traditions MTCD329–0, *The Hardy Sons of Dan*, and Veteran VT134CD, *Linkin' o'er the Lea* (Maggie Murphy, Fermanagh); and on Topic TSCD514, *A World Without Horses* (Walter Pardon, Norfolk). Pitts also printed a very different take on the story, 'The Devil in Search of a Wife' (Bodleian, Firth c.20(139)) which however includes the 'pattens' episode.

DICK TURPIN

Roud 856

Tune noted by Gamblin.

The real Dick Turpin, hanged for horse-theft on Saturday 7 April 1739 at York, was not the romantic hero of popular myth; though he did take care to die well-dressed and with dignity. It was the writer William Harrison Ainsworth, in his enormously popular historical romance *Rookwood* (1834), who re-invented the almost forgotten felon as the archetypal 'gentleman of the road', gave him a loyal steed called Black Bess, and credited to him the famous ride to York which was actually based on an incident described by Daniel Defoe in his *A Tour through the whole Island of Great Britain*, published in the mid 1720s. Defoe dated the incident to 1676, but there may have been other, similar stories even earlier. There had been romantic highwaymen before, but *Rookwood*, followed in 1840 by Henry Downes Miles' novel *Dick Turpin*, ensured the upstart Turpin's new position at the head of the league. Stage adaptations followed, and even an 'equestrian drama', *Turpin's Ride to York*, which features at a crucial point in Hardy's *Far from the Madding Crowd*.

Naturally, there were songs. This one is probably a product of the theatre or early music hall; there are no broadside copies earlier than around 1850, though it was published by many of the later printers, usually as 'My Bonny Black Bess', but also as 'Death of Black Bess' and 'Dick Turpin's Ride to York'. For examples, see Bodleian, Harding B 11(2517): Ryle of London; Harding B 11(3910): Howse of Worcester; Harding B 11(829): Such; 2806 c.13(200): Harkness of Preston; Johnson Ballads 560: E M A Hodges of London; Johnson Ballads 670: J Paul of London; 2806 b.11(230): Pearson of Manchester; and others without imprint.

Other Turpin songs have survived in greater numbers than this one, of which the only oral examples we have are from the Gardiner and Williams collections. Gardiner's sources had only fragmentary texts, so the version printed here is David Snugg's single verse (our first), amended from the text printed by Williams (101), which came from G Giles of Blunsdon Hill, Wiltshire. The rest of our text is from the same source, which is very close to broadside copies. Aged 70 in 1907, Mr Snugg was older than his song.

Further detail on Turpin and the songs based on his legend can be found in Graham Seal, *The Outlaw Legend: A Cultural Tradition in Britain, America and Australia* (Cambridge: Cambridge University Press, 1996). A good introduction to the historical context and the growth of the myth is James Sharpe, *Dick Turpin: The Myth of the English Highwayman* (London: Profile Books, 2004).

THE DOCKYARD GATE

Roud 1739

Tune noted by Guyer.

Only a few oral examples of this song are known, the majority sung by seafarers. Frank Kidson printed a tune with one verse from a Whitby sailor's daughter in *FSJ* II (9) 1906, 265, expressing the opinion that it was a 'real sailors' song' and likely composed 'on shipboard'. Maybe it was, but traditional texts all appear to derive from a broadside, 'Plymouth Sound', printed by Such in the 1860s or later; for copies of which, see Bodleian, Firth c.12(278), Harding B 11(3037) and Harding B 11(3036). Of course, the song may well be older than the Such printing; Baring-Gould printed a 'Plymouth Sound' tune to new words of his own (*Songs of the West*, revised edition, 1905, song number 54) and referred to a 'coarse and undesirable' broadside published by Keys of Devonport. It is not certain that was the same song, but the tune, noted from Roger Luxton at Halwill, Devon, does seem to be a relative of the melody printed by Kidson, and of ours.

Frederick Fennemore's text has been amended in places from the broadside. In verse 5, line 4, for instance, he sang obscurely: 'Or perhaps he is in the black list, our joys will never unfold'. Verse 3 here is added from the broadside, apparently a little modified from the version sung by Sam Larner of Norfolk, which can be heard on Topic TSCD511, *Now is the Time for Fishing*. Larner's tune is another relative.

DON'T LET ME DIE AN OLD MAID

Roud 802

One of those complex old songs found all over the English-speaking world that has existed in oral and print traditions for many centuries. It exists in a wide range of variants, the main theme having frequently been re-written around selections of existing stanzas. That prolific songwriter Martin Parker is certainly the author of one early version, 'The Wooing Maid' (*Roxburghe* III, 52), entered at Stationers' Hall in 1636, but as he was known to incorporate existing material into his work, this general theme and the stock of stanzas are probably earlier. Another broadside of *c*.1690, 'The Maid's Call to the Bachelors' (Pepys 5.194) incorporates several of the stanzas used by Parker.

The strand of the song in oral tradition to which our song belongs is delivered as a monologue by the longing maid, while another variety is a dialogue between mother and daughter: see H726, Moses Mills, 'Time to be Made a Wife' in *The Constant Lovers*, and Bodleian, Harding B 16(160a) and Harding B 16(76b) for editions by Catnach and Pitts. One stanza that occurs in all versions is the third one here in which she compares her situation with her sister's.

For broadside examples of our song as 'The Love-Sick Maid', see Bodleian, Harding B 11(2247) (Pitts); Firth c.20(30) (Catnach); Harding B 28(188) (Wright of Birmingham). Variants continued to be printed on broadsides in widely varying forms throughout the eighteenth and nineteenth centuries under a variety of titles; see, for instance, Bodleian, Harding B 11(2011) (Bebbington of Manchester) and 2806 c.9(8) (Brereton of Dublin): 'The Chimney Sweep's Wedding'. The sister's name goes from Helen to Kate to Janet. Parker called her Cicely, but scarcely a version has the same name as another.

William Miller began our verse 2:

Come all pretty maids, some older, some younger
In view of sweethearts I must not stop longer

These lines have been substituted in *Marrow Bones* from elsewhere, and we have found no trace of verses 1, 4 and 5 in the MSS or in other versions. Mr Miller's final verse had only three lines:

Come shoemaker, sailor, come tinker, come tailor
Come fiddler or fifer or drummer that's pretty
Don't let me die an old maid but take me for pity.

THE EVERLASTING CIRCLE

Roud 129

Tune noted by Parsonson.

A widespread and popular song existing in numerous forms, employing a variety of progressions to complete the circle after we get beyond the branches of the tree; though many versions only get part of the way there. Mr Lugg's version follows the broadside issued by Pitts, 'The Tree in the Wood', in that it ends with a man and a maid in bed, but his chorus is as printed on a later broadside, 'Where the Green Leaves Grows Around' (see Bodleian, Firth c.26(260)). The second verse here is adapted from one sung by William Mason (Gardiner H632), while the last two were added to complete the circle; similar lines occur in other versions.

Songs on the same lines exist in other countries; in Brittany, for example, there is 'Ar Parc Caer', in France 'Le Bois Joli' and in Denmark 'Langt Udi Skoven'. Wales has 'Ar y Bryn Daeth Pren' and Ireland 'The Rattling Bog'. For further information see James Reeves, *Idiom of the People* 211–12 and *Everlasting Circle* 101–104; and *FSJ* III (13) 1909, 276–8.

Examples from tradition can be heard on Musical Traditions MTCD311–2, *Up in the North, Down in the South* (Tom Newman, Oxfordshire) and MTCD303, *Plenty of Thyme* (Cyril Poacher, Norfolk: an Irish form, 'The Bog Down in the Valley').

A FAIR MAID WALKING IN HER GARDEN

Roud 264 Laws N42

A very widespread and typical broadside ballad on the popular 'broken token' theme that has undergone the classic evolutions. The earlier English broadsides of nine stanzas, titled 'The Sailor's Return', from which this version derives, probably date from the last decade of the eighteenth century. Such, followed by Disley, added an extra stanza. English broadside versions vary very little throughout the nineteenth century and oral versions reflect this, although titles can vary somewhat. For examples, see Bodleian, Harding B 25(1713): Evans of London, Harding B 11(3387): Pitts, Harding B 11(383): Cadman of Manchester, 'The Sailor's Return'; Harding B 17(180a): Ferraby of Hull, 'The Loyal Sailor'; Firth c.12(335): Such, and Harding B 40(15): Nugent of Dublin, 'Young & Single Sailor'.

Irish and Scottish versions have undergone much greater alteration, having lost some of the middle stanzas but acquired a total of five additional ones, some of which can be put down to the pens of editors like Christie and Ord. American versions, which are mostly more closely related to the Irish ones, vary even more with the addition of three extra stanzas different to the new Scottish ones.

No words were noted with Mrs Steer's fine tune (forms of which are frequently associated with this song), so it is set here to Mr Pomery's text, slightly amended in places.

No recordings from English tradition are available at present, but Scottish and Irish examples can be heard on Musical Traditions MTCD308, *Ythanside* (Daisy Chapman, Aberdeenshire: 'The Poor and Single Sailor'); MTCD325–6, *From Puck to Appleby* (Mary Cash, Wexford: 'Lady in Her Father's Garden'); MTCD329–0, *The Hardy Sons of Dan* and Veteran VT134CD, *Linkin' o'er the Lea* (Maggie Murphy, Fermanagh: 'Seven Years Since I Had a Sweetheart'); and on Topic TSCD660, *Who's That at My Bed Window?* (Sarah Anne O'Neill, Tyrone: 'Standing in yon Flowery Garden').

FAIR SUSAN I LEFT

Roud 1447

Aeolian mode.

'When Fair Susan I left, a favourite Sea Song'[1] was published by Catherine Fentum (416 or 417, near Bedford Street, Strand, London)[2] around 1785, apparently without composer details; though the online catalogue of the British Vocal Music Collection (Part 2: Individual Songs) at the University at Buffalo[3] adds the further information, also from a Fentum print, 'Sung by Mr Dignum At the Beef-Stake-Club, and the Anacreontic Society'. Charles Dignum (1765–1827) was a popular tenor of the day and a frequent performer at the Theatre Royal, Drury Lane and Vauxhall Gardens among other venues. A slightly later edition published by J Hewitt's Musical Repository (59 Maiden Lane, New York) can be seen online at the Lester Levy Sheet Music Collection. The lyric was printed on broadsides during the first half of the nineteenth century, but few folk song collectors noted it: beside four examples in Hammond and three in Gardiner, Sharp got three in Somerset; all these were sung to closely related tunes which, however, bear little obvious resemblance to the original music.

The tune as printed here is something of a hybrid. Frank Purslow tells us: 'Basically, Pomery had only the second half of Larcombe's tune, which he repeated to make enough music for a verse; but Larcombe's tune is in G major and Pomery sang his music in the Aeolian mode in A, so I compromised by using Larcombe's tune but transposing it into Aeolian in A.'[4]

The text is mostly collated from Larcombe and Pomery, with verse 6 added – a little modified – from the set noted by Gardiner (H99) from Richard Hall, Itchen Abbas, Hampshire, 1905:

The news reached her ears that the gallant ship was lost,
And her Thomas would be hers no more,
She died like a rose that was nipped by the frost,
And left me her loss to deplore.

There are various further editorial modifications, some made with reference to broadside copies; but all the singers, and all the broadsides we have seen, agree on some form of 'Whilst blue lightning all round us did fly [flash]' in verse 3, line 2; the thunder appears to be wholly editorial. For broadside copies, see among others Harding B 11(4122): Catnach, between 1813 and 1838; Harding B 16(85a): T Batchelar, between 1817 and 1828; 2806 c.17(118): W Armstrong, Liverpool, between 1820 and 1824; and Harding B 15(369a): J Wheeler, Manchester, between 1827 and 1847.

[1] British Library shelfmark G.316.l.(66.)
[2] Frank Kidson: *British Music Publishers, Printers and Engravers, London, Provincial, Scottish and Irish, from Queen Elizabeth's Reign to George the Fourth's*. London: W E Hill, 1900, 47.
[3] http://ublib.buffalo.edu/libraries/units/music/spcoll/bvm2.html
[4] Letter, Frank Purslow to Malcolm Douglas, 11 January 2007.

THE FEMALE CABIN-BOY

Roud 239 Laws N13

Tune noted by Guyer.

William Hill's text, like some other oral examples, lacks the usual concluding stanza; which consists of a toast to the heroine and a wish for a lot more like her. The punchline is the best place to finish a joke, after all. Broadside editions appear as 'The Female Cabin Boy' and 'The Handsome Cabin Boy'. See, for example, Bodleian, Firth c.12(443): Forth of Pocklington; Harding B 11(2620): Hillatt and Martin of London; Harding B 11(1186): Harkness of Preston; Firth b.25(546): Merry of Bedford; Firth c.12(266): Such of London; Firth c.13(232): White of Liverpool; Harding B 11(2764): Jones of Sheffield; and issues by Disley, Fortey and others. Irish issues include 2806 c.15(190): Birmingham of Dublin; Harding B 19(67): Nugent of Dublin; and 2806 c.18(54): Haly of Cork. A copy by Lindsay of Glasgow (ref Mu23–y1:035) is at the Glasgow Broadside Ballads website.

The song doesn't appear especially often in oral collections, but became very popular in the folk song revival in the 1960s, largely due to performances by A L Lloyd and Ewan MacColl; and, indeed, to the *Marrow Bones* printing. Oral versions in England seem to be largely confined to the south and East Anglia. It attained some popularity in Scotland and a few examples have been found in the USA and Canada. It was common enough in the mid-nineteenth century; a street ballad singer interviewed by Henry Mayhew in 'Narrative of a London Sneak, or Common Thief' (*London Labour and the London Poor*, vol IV, 302) mentioned it, and 'The Dark Eyed Sailor', as songs he often sang.

Some early broadsides, such as Hillatt and Martin, 'The Female Cabin Boy or, The Row Amongst the Sailors', add 'To the tune of: Female drummer'. Roy Palmer (*Boxing the Compass: Sea Songs and Shanties*, Todmorden: Herron Publishing, 2001, 209–10) prints a contemporary 'Female Drummer' tune from the poet John Clare's MSS, and this is clearly a relative of Mr Hill's tune, though the phrases of the latter appear in a different order; indeed, most traditional variants seem to be sung to forms of the same melody, though often rather changed. Also germane were the tunes used by Bob Hart (Suffolk), Jeannie Robertson (Aberdeenshire) and other versions as far apart as Somerset and Newfoundland. Recordings from oral tradition can be heard on Musical Traditions MTCD301–2, *A Broadside* (Bob Hart, 1969) and Topic TSCD662, *We've Received Orders to Sail* (Bob Hart, 1972); and Topic TSCD514, *A World Without Horses* (Walter Pardon).

THE FARMER'S TOAST

Roud 1603

Tune noted by Guyer.

Lines from this song, accompanied by mottoes such as 'God speed the plough', 'In God is all our Trust' and 'Industry Produceth Wealth', were frequently printed on ceramic mugs, jugs and cups from the mid-eighteenth century onward. Country singers have been known to take the words direct from a mug and set their own tunes to them, but longer texts such as Frank Gamblin's (the only example currently listed in the Roud Index apart from an Irish variant, 'The Jolly Farmer', presently classed separately at number 3043) derive from broadside editions of 'The Farmer'. For several examples, see Bodleian, Johnson Ballads 822: Pitts; Harding B 25(622): R Walker of Norwich; Harding B 25(622): [M W] Carrall of York; Harding B 11(1150); Harding B 19(69b); and 2806 c.8(171). The words also appeared in *The Universal Songster*, vol II, 218. Thomas Hardy knew the song, and mentions it as 'I have parks, I have hounds' in *Tess of the d'Urbervilles*.

Our text is little changed from Mr Gamblin's, though in verse 1 he sang: 'My jorum is quiet now boys we will try it'; this was amended to the more coherent 'My glass is now dry so to sing we will try', but broadsides show that Gamblin had mis-remembered the line 'One jorum *in* quiet my boys we will try it'. In verse 2, the lines have been rearranged to make better sense. Gardiner's text transcription suggests that Gamblin sang his final half-stanza to the first part of the tune, but using the second part, as indicated here, is perhaps more effective. 'The singer', wrote Gardiner, 'called this a freemason's song'. It may well have been sung at masonic gatherings, as also at harvest homes and the like; and, as Hardy attests, in ordinary workaday situations. 'The tune', Gardiner added, 'which is familiar, I cannot identify.' Gardiner may perhaps have been thinking of 'Molly Malone', with which the first part of the tune shares some similarities, though the melodic progression is common enough. In the original edition, the music text began 'Come all *you* jolly fellows' and the third quaver in bar 2 was split into two semiquavers to accommodate 'you', which however was neither in the main text nor the MS. We have removed it, and restored the quaver.

THE FRIAR IN THE WELL

Roud 116 Child 276

This song was first entered in the Stationers' Register on 1 June 1629, but surviving broadside copies of 'The Fryer well-fitted: Or, A pretty Jest that once befell, How a Maid put a Fryer to cool in the Well' are later; see Bodleian, 4o Rawl. 566(63) for an edition printed *c.*1663–1674; Douce Ballads 1(85a) for one issued twenty or so years later, and Wood E 25(86) for another, without imprint. Child (V, 100–103) prints as his version A the broadside text published by Coles, Vere and Wright of London (first reference above) with variations noted from two close versions: a slightly later broadside from Thackeray and Passinger, and the text printed in *Pills* III, 1719, 325–6, as 'The Fryer and the Maid'.

The story appears to be older still. Anthony Munday's play *Downfall of Robert, Earl of Huntington* (1601, act 4 scene 2) mentions the 'merry jest ... how the friar fell into the well', and John Skelton's satire *Colyn Cloute* contains the lines

> But when the freare fell in the well
> He coud not syng himselfe thereout...

Skelton (tutor to the future Henry VIII) died in 1529. We can't tell, though, whether these are references to an earlier form of the song or to a folktale on which it may have been based. Child wondered whether it might ultimately be traceable back to a Persian story in the *Túti Náma* (*c.*1335) of Ziya al-Din Nakhshabí, in which a bed is laid over a dry well as a trap for unwelcome suitors. However that may be, stories and songs in which corrupt churchmen get a suitably humiliating comeuppance have always been popular, and this song was reprinted from time to time over a long period. J Johnson of Goodramgate, York, issued it in the nineteenth century and there is a more modern version on a broadside without imprint in Manchester Central Library.

Examples from tradition, however, are very rare. Child printed a Scottish text from the unreliable Peter Buchan, correlated with two from George Kinloch's MSS which may merely have been revisions of Buchan's version; and the Hammonds got, beside our set from Mr Penny, a tune without words from Frank Stockley of Wareham, Dorset (D661). More recently (1989) Gwilym Davies recorded a version from Charlie Hill of Spreyton, Devon. Mr Penny's incomplete text has been condensed from two-line stanzas in which the first line of each was repeated three times, to a more manageable series of four-line stanzas. Various editorial changes have been made; some are minor cosmetic touches or re-arrangements of lines to fill gaps, but the following original readings ought to be noted:

Verse 1, line 2:
    He courted a maid most wonderful bold

Verse 2, lines 3–4:
    Oh no, says the friar, you know very well
    That I can sing your soul out of hell

Verse 4, lines 1–2:
    How far to shun the friar the maid couldn't tell
    So she placed a sheet all over the well

Verse 5, lines 2–4:
    Oh now, says the maid, my father's a-coming.
    So under the sheet the old friar did creep
    And into the well he chanced for to slip

Verse 6:
    Oh the friar called out with a pitiful sound
    Oh help me out or I shall be drowned.
    Oh no, says the maid, you know very well
    You said you would sing my soul out of hell.
    Now you sing yourself out of the well.

Verse 8, line 2:
    And he dropped alas [his arse] like a new-washen sheep

A few lines were missing from Mr Penny's version: verse 4, line 4 and verse 5, line 1, seem to be wholly editorial; while verse 8, lines 3–4, are adapted from the texts in Child. Mr Penny's tune, which Bertrand Bronson (Bronson IV, 140–142) described as 'rollicking', is not related to the melody printed in John Playford's *English Dancing Master* (1651) as 'The Maid peept out at the window, or the Frier in the Well', to which early versions were presumably sung. See also Simpson, 240–242.

THE FURZE FIELD

Roud 1037

Tune noted by Gamblin.

A scarce song known only in three versions, but likely from some early nineteenth-century broadside when such euphemistic pieces were common; although that type of song was also popular in the eighteenth and seventeenth centuries, and goes back at least to the early days of printing. Other examples of the genre from the Gardiner collection are 'The Mower' (Roud 833: see 'The Buxom Lass' in *The Wanton Seed*) and 'The Bonny Black Hare' (Roud 1656: see *The Constant Lovers*).

In verse 3, line 5, Moses Mills repeated 'Your hooks and your angles all at your command' from the previous verse; the substitution here is editorial. Beside our version, another was printed in *English Dance and Song*, 55 (3) autumn 1993, 15–16, as 'The Old Sportsman'; it was noted by Horace Harman in Buckinghamshire, some time between 1918 and 1935. George Dunn of Birmingham's fragmentary set, 'I've Got a Warren', can be heard on Musical Traditions MTCD317–8, *Chainmaker*.

THE GAME OF ALL FOURS

Roud 232

Tune noted by Balfour Gardiner.

All Fours (also called Seven Up) was a game for four players rather than two; not unlike Whist. It is first, we gather, mentioned in Charles Cotton's *Complete Gamester*, 1674. The main object was to take the Jack of Trumps (it is from All Fours that the Knave acquired its new name of Jack); the winning score of seven points being counted in the order of 'High, Low, Jack and the Game'. It became fashionable again in the nineteenth century, providing easily recognisable imagery for this mildly erotic broadside song, which was printed by Pitts, Birt and then Disley in London. Walker of Durham and Pearson of Manchester also issued it, and there are a number of editions without imprint. See Bodleian, Harding B 11(1855): Pitts, 'The Cards'; Harding B 11(540): Birt, 'The Cards'; and, without imprint, Firth b.34(120) and Firth b.34(281), 'Game of All Fours'.

The text here is mostly Fred Osman's, amended in places from William Randall's. Mr Osman's heroine hails, as she does in broadsides, from Windsor; in Mr Randall's version she is from Croydon. Known oral versions are all from the southern half of England, and are usually sung to forms of the same tune; the song has lasted in tradition to the present day, with recent examples coming mostly from Travellers. Gardiner (1905) noted that it was 'also sung in Norfolk', and Sam Larner recalled that it was well known there in the early years of the twentieth century.

Examples from oral tradition can be heard on Musical Traditions MTCD309–10, *Just Another Saturday Night* (Sarah Porter, Sussex) and MTCD317–8, *Chainmaker* (George Dunn, Warwickshire); Topic Records TSCD 661, *My Father's the King of the Gypsies* (Levi Smith, Surrey) and TSCD511, *Now is the Time for Fishing* (Sam Larner); and Veteran VT136CD, *The Yellow Handkerchief* (Phoebe Smith, Suffolk).

GAMEKEEPERS LIE SLEEPING

Roud 363

Tune noted by Guyer.

Popular in southern England, though no broadside version has survived. Frank Kidson printed a version from unusually far north (Goole), 'Hares in the Old Plantation' in his *Traditional Tunes* which, though incomplete, has more form to it than most examples and is possibly closer to the original; but there is considerable variation between versions, indicating that it has been in oral tradition for some time. It has been particularly popular among Travellers, and James Ray, from whom most of our text came, was described by Gardiner as 'a 21 year old gipsy'. Charles Bull, who provides our tune, also had a fairly full set of words.

Mr Ray began: 'I got a dog and a very good dog is he', which is here regularised from other versions. His second verse (not included here) was the same, with 'gun' substituted for 'dog'. Our verse 3 began:

> I says to my dog we'll have no more of that
> My dog took after him there

This is amended here from the Copper Family version, which also provides our verse 4. In verse 5, Mr Ray's final line was 'For the gamekeeper is coming', and his second line in verse 6 was 'Across the open plantation'. He followed this with:

I says unto this labouring man
Will you buy this hare for one crown?
For a crown of bran I will lay down
Brave boys, if you'll bring fifty.

'Crown of bran' is 'crown a brace' in other versions. The final verse is also slightly amended. Ray's and Bull's tunes were similar; most examples of this song are sung to divergent variants of the same melody, forms of which also carry English versions of 'Barbara Allen' (Roud 54 Child 84). Recordings from tradition can be heard on Musical Traditions MTCD400, *Down the Cherry Tree* (George Maynard, Sussex); MTCD307, *Band of Gold* (Wiggy Smith, Gloucestershire); Topic TSCD668, *To Catch a Fine Buck was My Delight* (Bob Roberts, Isle of Wight, and Wiggy Smith); TSCD600, *Hidden English* (Tom Willett, Kent); and Coppersongs CD2, *Coppersongs 2* (Copper Family, Sussex).

GOSSIP JOAN

Roud 1039

The earliest surviving version is found in *Pills* (VI, 315–6) under the title 'The Woman's Complaint to her Neighbour'. The tune was used as a vehicle for many other comic songs, particularly in the comic operas of the eighteenth century (in Gay's *Beggar's Opera* it was sung to 'Why, how now, Madam Flirt?') but it appears to have survived in oral tradition since 1720 with little aid from print. A broadside version of five stanzas, 'Gossip Jones' was printed in America (see item as102120 at the *America Singing* website of the Library of Congress (http://lcweb2.loc.gov/ammem/amsshtml/). In volume 12 of the Madden Collection is 'The Sequel to Gossip Joan, A Comic Song, by Mr A Bradley' with eleven stanzas, the tune and even a guitar accompaniment. Though no imprint is present, the type is of the style of the mid-eighteenth century and a companion piece, obviously by the same printer, was by George Alexander Stevens (1710–1780).

Oral examples are mostly English, and include verses from the *Pills* text as well as others. Joseph Vincent's fifth verse is almost exactly the same, and his first and final verses little changed. The suggested alternative ending is from a version printed by Williams (41–2). The tunes have diverged considerably since D'Urfey's time, but there is still a recognisable relationship between Mr Vincent's and the melody heard today at hunt song nights in the Pennines, an example of which can be heard on EFDSS CD02, *A Century of Song* (Will Noble and John Cocking, Yorkshire).

GREEN BUSHES

Roud 1040 Laws P2

Two verses of this song appeared in John Baldwin Buckstone's drama *The Green Bushes; or, A Hundred Years Ago*, first produced at the Adelphi, London in 1845, where they were sung by Mrs Fanny Fitzwilliam in the rôle of Nelly O'Neil. The play was an enormous success and was regularly revived over the years, becoming a staple of touring repertory companies; which may go some way toward accounting for the song's popularity, and the stability of its text, in oral tradition. The song was not original to the play; it was published by Catnach, Pitts and most of the usual provincial printers of the nineteenth century, though not in Ireland. Broadside versions vary from four to six stanzas, mostly six, and are quite standard. They appear under two titles; for examples, see Bodleian, Harding B 11(53) (Pitts) and Firth c.18(145) (no imprint): 'The False Lover'; and, among others, Harding B 20(64) (Harkness of Preston), 2806 c.17(157) (Kiernan of Manchester) and Harding B 11(1416) (McCall of Liverpool): 'Green Bushes'.

The song is found in the USA, Canada and Scotland, but is much more common in England. It has a companion broadside called 'Among the Green Bushes' with which it is sometimes confused, but which tells a quite different story. Our second verse is not from George Dowden, and doesn't appear on broadsides, but it occurs regularly in oral versions. Ishmael Cornish's tune is not the usual one: 'I have never heard this tune,' noted Henry Hammond, 'or seen it'. We have added two variant notes from the MS in the final two bars. Recordings from tradition can be heard on Musical Traditions MTCD305–6, *Put a Bit of Powder on it Father* (Walter Pardon, Norfolk) and MTCD303, *Plenty of Thyme* (Cyril Poacher, Suffolk); Veteran VT136CD, *The Yellow Handkerchief* (Phoebe Smith, Suffolk); and Topic TSCD651, *Come Let Us Buy the Licence* (Geoff Ling, Suffolk).

THE GREY HAWK

Roud 293

This song appears on seventeenth-century broadsides as 'Cupid's trappan; or Up the Green Forest'. It was narrated from a woman's point of view but there was at least one male counterpart, 'The Bachelor's Fore-cast; or Cupid Unblest'. The former is in most of the surviving collections of this period and versions can be found on the Bodleian Broadside Ballads website (see Douce Ballads 1(50a), 4o Rawl. 566(111) and Douce Ballads 1(39b)). The latter is in *The Euing Collection of English Broadside Ballads* (University of Glasgow, 1971, number 16) and is reprinted with the former in *Roxburghe* VII, 359 and 361. The rivalry between the sexes in these spawned a whole sequence of sequels or answers, to the same tune.

Under the title 'Cupid's Trapan' it was reprinted by Dicey and Marshall in the mid-eighteenth century. By the time Pitts got hold of it in the early C19, it had been reduced from nineteen stanzas to six, and he titled it 'Bonny Boy'. Catnach also printed it, and then (in very similar forms) Such, Collard of Bristol, Williams of Portsea and Wrigley of Manchester, but it was not widely published. For examples, see Bodleian, Harding B 25(254) (Jennings of London); Firth c.18(127) (Pitts); and Johnson Ballads 475 (Hodges).

Our final verse seems to have evolved from one of the songs set to the same tune, 'The Patient Husband and the Scolding Wife', the sixth stanza of which commences, 'Thrice happy is he that hath a good wife, but far better off the young man ...' (See Chappell, II, 1859, 555–7). Simpson (151–153) discusses the tune's history, noting that traditional survivals are sung to different music.

The eventual transformation of 'Bonny Boy' into 'Grey hawk' is not difficult to imagine, considering all the bird imagery in the original. The song appears to be uniformly spread across England, Scotland and North America; as one would expect of such a venerable ballad, it varies widely. Robert Barratt's first verse had an additional two lines:

> And I got a little bell and tied it to her toe
> Thinking she would fly not away.

The first two lines of each subsequent verse were repeated. Here, the additional lines and repeats have been omitted. A recording from tradition can be heard on Musical Traditions MTCD311–2, *Up in the North and Down in the South* (Bob Blake, Sussex). See also the notes to 'My Bonny, Bonny Boy'.

THE GREY MARE

Roud 680 Laws P8

Tune noted by Gamblin.

Issued under a number of titles by a number of nineteenth-century broadside printers in Lancashire, Yorkshire and Newcastle, while in the south only Pitts, Batchelar, Jennings and Such of London produced copies. Coverley of Boston printed it in the USA with 'Roger' changed to 'Johnny'. For broadsides examples, see Bodleian, Harding B 11(4390): Forth of

Pocklington and others without imprint ('Young Roger and the Grey Mare'); 2806 c.16(50): Swindells of Manchester; Harding B 25(1645): Harkness of Preston; Harding B 25(1647): Jennings of London ('Roger the Miller and the Grey Mare'); Harding B 28(45): Armstrong of Liverpool ('The Farmer's Grey Mare'); and Harding B 11(1435): Pitts; Harding B 11(1434): Such ('Grey Mare').

Oral versions are widespread all over North America, but the song doesn't appear very often in England, where it presumably originated around 1800. Kidson (78) mentions that his mother heard it sung at Otley, in Yorkshire, about the year 1826–27, and adds that it was still current among old people in other parts of the country at the time of writing. It has also turned up occasionally in Scotland, Wales and Ireland. Later broadsides pare the story down a little, and cut back the eight-line stanzas to quatrains, as in this version; where Mr Oliver's text has been amended in places, and most of verse 3 added, from a text without tune probably noted from a Mr(?) Whittier.

The renowned singer Phil Tanner can be heard singing a version, 'Young Roger Esquire', on EFDSS CD002, *A Century of Song* and on Veteran VT145CD, *The Gower Nightingale*.

THE GRUMBLING FARMERS

Roud 1390

Tune noted by E Quintrell.

Very rare in oral tradition. Only three examples are known: this one from Cornwall, one in Alfred Williams' MSS from Wiltshire, and a Cheshire version. It was quite widely printed on broadsides, with editions appearing in London, Birmingham, Manchester, Preston, Newcastle, Belfast and Edinburgh. It was issued by Evans of London and Marshall of Newcastle, which would probably place its origins in the late eighteenth century. For a later edition by J K Pollock of North Shields, see Bodleian, Harding B 25(783).

Mr Boaden had learned this song from 'a Mr Curry of Helston, long deceased'. Quintrell noted the tune and words in some detail, and included a few indications of the local pronunciation, such as taelk'd, wärs, owld, poorch, glowriously, furbid, and rāgardless. In the original edition, the chorus was incorrectly shown as ending each time with a repeat of the last two lines of verse 1; in fact the final two lines of each verse are repeated in the corresponding chorus, and we have shown this in the song text.

HOME DEAREST HOME

Roud 269 Laws K43

Only seven broadside printings survive: three in London and one each in Birmingham, Cork, Belfast and Edinburgh. English versions all seem to derive from Pitts' seven-stanza 'The Servant of Rosemary Lane', which has no evidence of a chorus. The Belfast Poet's Box edition, though a stanza longer, is rather garbled and repetitive; it does, however, retain an echo of the chorus 'and the ash and the oak and the bonnie willow tree' in its final verse. Baird of Cork's version ('The Boys of Cork City') develops, after the third stanza, into a mélange of commonplaces, largely from 'The Boys of Kilkenny', *q.v.* Curiously, the later version from Sanderson of Edinburgh ('Home, Dear Home') also develops in a similar fashion into a different set of commonplaces, mostly relating to 'Bonny Udny'; which also happens to be related to 'The Boys of Kilkenny'. This is the only broadside to give the chorus, which was probably added from one of various Scottish songs that include forms of it; though of course it also appeared in English songs as far back as the seventeenth century. The trio of trees usually start with oak and ash, but the third tree can be the willow, birch, ivy, elm, rowan and so on. For broadside examples, see Bodleian, Harding B 11(4221) (Pitts); Johnson Ballads 624 (Jennings); Harding B 15(279a) (Disley); and Harding B 17(130a) (Sanderson).

Being popular with seamen, oral versions have spread rapidly around the English-speaking world so it is very widespread. A navy version, 'Bell-Bottom Trousers', was a commercial success during WWII and it became very popular in the armed forces. Mildly bawdy versions also appear in song collections. It has been very popular in North America, and there has even been a cowboy parody. An example of the 'Rosemary Lane' branch, sung by William Bartlett, is in *The Wanton Seed*.

William Chubb's text has been amended in places. His fifth verse ran:

But if it be a girl you shall dangle it on your knee
But if it be a boy you shall put him to [the] sea
With his long quarter shoes and his jacket so blue
He shall walk the quarter-deck as his daddy used to do.

The song, Mr Chubb remarked, had been 'sung in the Navy fifty years ago'. Recordings from tradition can be heard on Musical Traditions MTCD309–10, *Just Another Saturday Night* (Jack Arnoll, Sussex) and Topic TSCD652, *My Ship Shall Sail the Ocean* (Jumbo Brightwell, Suffolk).

I Live Not Where I Love

Roud 593

This song derives from 'The Constant Lover' (see *Roxburghe* I, 212–6) 'to a Northerne Tune Called *Shall the absence of my Mistresse*'. It was registered at Stationers' Hall in 1638, but the basic idea and the all-important last line came from the pen of Robert Southwell in 1595. 'The Constant Lover' is ascribed to 'P L' on the broadside; Baring-Gould and Simpson take this to be Peter Lowberry. The first two verses of Robert Barratt's version are 1 and 5 of the twelve stanzas of the broadside, and his third verse corresponds to the ninth.

In the early nineteenth century, Pitts printed a four-stanza version almost word for word as ours, and this, the most common form, was reprinted in York, Bristol, Liverpool and North Shields. Williams of Portsea also printed it, and this is a likely source for Barratt's version. Pitts and Jennings also printed a rewritten text split into seven quatrains, with a chorus which is the second half of our first stanza. Its title is 'The Maiden's Tears for the Loss of her Truelove, Harry'. It lacks the first part of the second stanza and in syntax is quite different to Pitts' other version. See Bodleian, Harding B 11(39) (Pitts) and Harding B 25(882) (Croshaw of York); and for 'The Maiden's Tears', Harding B 17(184a).

Chappell (II, 451–3) prints a West Country tune very close to Mr Barratt's, commenting, 'I have been favoured with copies from various and widely distant parts of the country.' Fifty years later, the song seemed largely to have been forgotten, and Barratt's is the only full oral version of the nineteenth-century broadside. There is a 2 stanza version from Sussex in *FSJ* I (5) 1904 273, and Sharp found one-and-a-half stanzas in Somerset. Mr Barratt made a valiant attempt to sing from a man's perspective, substituting 'her' for 'him' in several places, but couldn't do much about the last two lines.

The Indian Lass

Roud 2326

Ionian, with inflexion of 4th.

Printed on nineteenth-century broadsides beginning with Catnach, followed by other London and provincial printers and De Marsan of New York. See, for example, Bodleian, Firth c.12(279): Such; Johnson Ballads 436: Fortey; Harding B 11(1759): Samuel Russell of Birmingham; Harding B 11(1757): Harkness of Preston; Firth c.12(279): De Marsan of New York. The texts vary little.

Evidently very popular in its day, oral examples have been found mostly in England

(Gardiner got five, and the Hammonds two) with others in Canada and a couple in Ireland. In the USA – and to a degree in Canada – the song is little known, tradition preferring its enormously popular and rather more chaste relative, 'The Little Mohee' (Roud 275, Laws H8). It would be surprising if the song did not appeal to sailors, and Captain Love, aged 70 when the Hammonds met him, was a retired mariner. The Captain's text is amended in places from broadside copies; his verse 4 began:

> A glass of good liquor I gave in her hand
> Kind sir, you are welcome to this In-di-an.

Our verse 4 omits those lines. As printed, it is a conflation of two from the broadside (quoted here from the Such edition):

> With a glass of good liquor she welcomed me in
> Kind sir you are welcome to have anything.
> But as I embraced her, this was her tone
> You are a poor sailor and far from your home.
>
> We tossed and we tumbled in each others arms
> And all that long night I embraced her sweet charms.
> With rural enjoyment the time passed away
> I did not go to leave her till nine the next day.

Captain Love continued:

> The day was appointed we were going away
> All on the wide ocean to lead her astray...

The second line (which was evidently mis-remembered) is dropped here, and our verse 5 begins with an adaptation of an unused line from the broadside; although 'mutual enjoyment' makes good sense, it appears to be editorial, and some singers may well prefer the more evocative 'rural enjoyment'. A traditional example can be heard on Veteran VT140CD, *Good Order* (Velvet Brightwell, Suffolk).

THE INNKEEPER'S DAUGHTER

Roud 917 Laws P4

Presumably an English broadside piece; Purslow's original notes stated 'Published on eighteenth-century broadsides', but we have not so far located any. Versions vary considerably, so it has probably been in oral tradition since the early nineteenth century at any rate. Very much a southern English song; Sharp's Somerset versions set it in Watchet and Bristol (and less obvious locales such as Threepenny Street), Hampshire versions set it in Gosport, and Dorset versions in Plymouth. It was also popular in Nova Scotia, where it is set in London, while a New York State version sets it in Bristol.

Verse 2 here is introduced from elsewhere; probably adapted from a verse in Gardiner H711 ('In Fair Gosport City', from George Baldwin) which ran:

> She was courted by a sailor, a sailor indeed
> A jolly Jack tar and John was his name
> And just as they appointed for their wedding day
> He received orders and sailed away.

Mr Bridle's text has been polished up in places; for instance, in verse 6, 'he shooked her by the hand'. Also in that verse, the original edition gave line 2 as 'How do they know that their sport might be spoiled'; 'that' appears to have been a mistake for the MS 'but', and we have restored the MS reading, which makes better sense. Similarly, in verse 8, line 2, we have amended the apparent omission in '... to give bride away' to Mr Bridle's original 'to give the bride away'. A 'Watchet Sailor' version, from the traditional singer George Withers of Somerset, can be heard on Veteran VTC5CD, *When the Wind Blows*.

JOHN APPLEBY

Roud 1292

A late eighteenth-century song, loosely based on Martin Parker's 'John and Joan: or, A mad couple well met' from the time of Charles I (see *Roxburghe* I, 503). The earliest modern version was printed by Laurie & Whittle of London in 1805 (see Bodleian, Johnson Ballads fol. 75) and then by Pitts (Bodleian, Firth c.22(103)), Marshall of Newcastle and Collard of Bristol. It also appeared in *The Universal Songster*, vol I (1825) 385, with an engraving by George Cruikshank. Laurie & Whittle and Marshall have six stanzas and Pitts, five.

The song was popularised by John Fawcett (1768–1837), an actor and singer particularly associated with the Theatre Royal, Covent Garden and the Haymarket Theatre. Broadwood (132–133) printed a version from Sussex, also in 9/8, learned 'from Kentish hop-pickers', and speculated that it might have been 'a political song, directed against Oliver Cromwell'; on the whole, this seems rather unlikely. The Hammonds also noted a fragment (tune and one verse) from William Bartlett, and Williams (225–6) printed a text from Gloucestershire.

William Miller's tune has been simplified a little in bars 4 and 5. In verse 4, line 7, he sang 'We'll all get merry tonight'; the broadsides, however, insist on 'drunk'.

JOHN BLUNT

Roud 115 Child 275

Based on an ancient folktale known all over Europe and going back beyond the advent of print, this song exists in distinct Scottish and English versions, both traceable back to the eighteenth century. It was probably made into a song some time in the C17, but no broadside copies from this period have survived. In England it was printed in twelve stanzas as 'John Blunt' in 1785 by J Wallis of Larkspur Street, London (see Bodleian, Douce Prints S 9(p. 208)), with the tune and a detailed engraving of the travellers pulling the old lady out of the bed. The tune is close to Mrs Seale's but the last two lines are repeated to a different strain. Such's seems to be the only other London broadside, but that is essentially the Scottish text printed in *SMM* III, 1790, number 300. Williams of Portsea printed eleven stanzas, and there were plenty of editions in Scotland and Newcastle during the nineteenth century. A broadside without imprint, Johnson Ballads 2597, is another printing of the English form of the song.

Oral tradition shows many examples in Scotland and the USA with a few in Canada, but Mrs Seale's is the only English one we know of, apart from a three-verse fragment Sharp got from a Mr George Humphreys in Marylebone Workhouse in 1914; and that begins in the Scottish manner. See also Bronson III, 130–139 and Child V, 96–99.

KING WILLIAM AND THE KEEPER

Roud 853

The earliest broadside example was published in 1696, during the reign of William III, by C Bates in Pye Corner, London (*Euing Collection* number 156) as 'The Loyal Forrister; or, Royal Pastime'. This twenty-stanza version continued to be printed by the likes of Dicey and Marshall of London into the mid-eighteenth century under the title 'The King and the Forrester' (see Bodleian, Harding B 6(75)), but it doesn't appear to have been taken up by nineteenth-century printers, probably because its length and subject were no longer in fashion by then. Songs about royal encounters with commoners were staple fare when the Robin Hood ballads were at the height of their popularity in the seventeenth century.

A few, mostly fragmentary, versions survived into the twentieth century. George Roper's text is augmented here from the version sung by George 'Pop' Maynard; specifically, verses 1, 6 and 12–16 are from Maynard, though lines 1–2 of our verse 12 had escaped his memory, and are supplied from the broadside. In verse 3, Mr Roper sang

> But the King made answer that 'twas not a man
> That would tell his business to any woman.

These lines have been replaced from Mr Maynard's text, which was printed in Ken Stubbs, *The Life of a Man*, London: EFDS, 1970, 44–5. Gardiner got a fragment (tune and one verse) from Albert Doe (H1334), and Sam Larner also had one verse. A version from the traditional singer Joseph Jones (Kent) can be heard on *Here's Luck to a Man* (Musical Traditions MTCD320).

JUST AS THE TIDE WAS FLOWING

Roud 1105

Printed in London by Catnach and his successors; the only two provincial editions are from Barr of Leeds and Sanderson of Edinburgh. All use the title '[Just as the] Tide is Flowing', except for Disley and Fortey who changed 'is' to 'was'. All produced a fairly standard six stanzas as in our Dorset version, which is very close indeed to the broadside texts. See Bodleian, Harding B 11(3634) (Catnach); Harding B 11(1952) (Fortey); Harding B 11(1951); Firth c.12(274) (Such); and Johnson Ballads 1837 (Barr).

The song is quite scarce in oral tradition, though Sharp found five versions in Somerset. It has also turned up in Norfolk, Cambridgeshire, Yorkshire, Hampshire and Newfoundland. The tune appears as 'The Peacock' in James Aird's *Selection of Scots, English, Irish and Foreign Airs*, II, 1782; and in several Irish collections of the early C19 such as O'Farrell's *Pocket Companion for the Irish or Union Pipes*, IV, 1810. At around the same time it was taken up by morris dancers, who know it as 'The Blue-eyed Stranger'. A recording from tradition can be heard on Topic TSCD62, *We've Received Orders to Sail* (Harry Cox, Norfolk).

THE LARK IN THE MORNING

Roud 151

There appear to be two distinct broadside versions, which differ in their final three stanzas. The earlier, 'The Plowman's Glory', can be found in an Edinburgh garland dated 1779; this version was also printed by Kendrew of York and there is one without imprint in the Madden Collection. The stanzas dropped by the later printers tell of Molly and Dolly (and their friends) being treated to cake at the wake by their ploughboy amours.

These romantic pastoral stanzas, so typical of the eighteenth century, have been replaced in the later version by more down-to-earth nineteenth-century commonplaces involving tumbling in new-mown hay, followed by the inevitable thickening in the waist, and with 'a health to the ploughboys' to finish. The later form was printed in London by Paul and then Catnach, Pitts and their successors, and in the north in Manchester and Leeds. See Bodleian, Harding B 25(1507): 'A New Song, Called The Plough Boy' (no imprint); Firth b.34(224) (Such); Firth c.18(172) (Disley); Harding B 25(1070) (Swindells of Manchester); Harding B 11(2060) (Bebbington of Manchester); and Harding B 11(3684) (no imprint): 'The Lark in the Morning'.

Most oral examples seem to derive from this later broadside version. They are widespread in England and Ireland but scarce in North America, where nineteenth-century ploughboys (*Oklahoma!* notwithstanding) probably had fewer such social – and sexual – opportunities. Baring-Gould printed a version in *A Garland of Country Song*, commenting 'Some [versions] have grafted onto them two or three objectionable stanzas. With these they appear in broadside, and begin: "As I was a-walking one morning in May" … But I have never heard any singers begin thus. They have invariably started with

"The lark in the morn."' Some did, certainly; but George Roper (and, indeed, many other singers) was made of sterner stuff and sang the whole thing. His text here is amended, mostly in small particulars only, but his first verse is re-cast on the lines of edited versions published by Sharp and others, so we quote his original words, very close to the broadside form:

> As I was a-walking one morning in May
> I heard a fair damsel these words for to say
> Of all the callings whatever they may be
> There's no life like the ploughboy's all in the month of May.

Recordings from tradition can be heard on Topic TSCD534, *Come Write Me Down* (Bob and Ron Copper, Sussex) and TSCD655, *Come My Lads that Follow the Plough* (Paddy Tunney, Fermanagh).

THE LIGHT OF THE MOON

Roud 21234 (formerly 179)

There is a large group of 'night-visiting' songs in which the cock crows an hour too soon and the heroine, thinking that day has come, sends her lover away by moonlight. These tend to be classed together as 'The Grey Cock, or, Saw You My Father?' (Roud 179 Child 248) following Child's title, but in fact a whole series of songs are involved; some are simple romantic interludes between lovers of ordinary flesh and blood, while in others one partner is a ghost, bound by folkloric convention to leave at cock-crow. The songs exchange verses among themselves, and frequently one is mistaken for another; with the result that there are people who believe that almost any song featuring lovers and a cock-crow must necessarily have a spectre lurking behind it. Hugh Shields cast valuable light (and some cold water) on this idea in his paper '"The Grey Cock": Dawn Song or Revenant Ballad?' (*Ballad Studies*, ed. E B Lyle, Mistletoe Series, Cambridge and Totowa, NJ: D S Brewer; Rowman and Littlefield for the Folklore Society, 1976, 67–92).

'Saw You My Father' first appeared in print in the latter part of the eighteenth century, and our song, with which it shares the cock-crow episode, at much the same time. A slip in the Madden Collection, 'A New Love Song' ((Slip Songs H–N [VWML microfilm 72, item 1238]) includes Farmer Mills' verses 1, 2, 4, 5 and 6. Our text, set to Robert Barratt's tune, is mainly from Mills, amended in places from Barratt. Only the first line of Mills' verse 4 survives, so Barratt's verse is used here, a little re-written. He actually sang:

> Oh 'twas all the forepart of the night
> We did both sport and play, play so pretty, play so pretty, play
> And all the last part of the night
> She sleeped in my arms till day.

Reeves, *Everlasting Circle*, 136–8, quotes both texts, remarking upon the similarity of Mills' sixth verse to the famous 'Western Wind' fragment:

> Westron wynde when wylle thow blow
> The smalle rayne downe can Rayne
> Cryst yf my love were in my Armys
> And I yn my bed Agayne.

Anne Gilchrist (*FSJ* VIII (34) 1930, 199–201) compares the tune to 'Queen Eleanor's Confession' (Chappell, I, 174), to a Manx version, and to the Methodist tune 'Portsmouth New'; and suggests that the repetitions of 'fallow' and so on might suggest 'a relic of an old glee setting'.

LIMBO

Roud 969

Tune noted by Gamblin, revised and checked by Guyer and G Leake, 5 June 1909. Mixolydian/Ionian, with inflexion of 7th.

J Woodfall Ebsworth (*Roxburghe* VIII, 811) refers to a version, with music, in *The Merry Musician c.*1729 (Baring-Gould found it in an earlier edition of 1716), and prints a white letter broadside of fourteen stanzas without imprint, 'The Fantastical Prodigal', from the Roxburghe Collection. It must have been popular later in that century, as it was printed on garlands as 'The Spendthrift; or The Young Man Clap'd in Limbo' with some considerable textual variation both from one edition to another and from earlier versions. Jennings and Pitts printed a ten-stanza slip, 'The Rake's Complaint in Limbo', in the early nineteenth century; see Bodleian, Harding B 11(3214), the most legible of three from Pitts.

Oral versions are scarce. Harker (257–9) prints an eleven-stanza example of the early nineteenth century and Baring-Gould included a set from 'an old charwoman in S Devon' in *English Minstrelsie* II, 1895, 32; the tune, he noted, was 'undoubtedly the same ... but ... somewhat modernised in transmission through two centuries.' In the twentieth century, apart from our Hampshire version, there is a seven-stanza Nova Scotia set in Helen Creighton's *Maritime Folk Songs* (Toronto: Ryerson Press,1962, 124), sung to a variant of the same tune, and Sharp collected a version (unpublished) in Gloucestershire.

James Brooman's text has been amended slightly from broadside copies. The first half of his first verse has wandered in from a quite different broadside song, 'The Unfortunate Lad'; for which, see Bodleian, Johnson Ballads 2943. Limbo, of course, is the Debtor's Prison.

THE LOWLANDS OF HOLLAND

Roud 484

Tune originally noted by Gamblin, 1907, and checked by Guyer; new notation by Vaughan Williams, January 1909. Aeolian, no 6th. The original Eb indication has been removed from the key signatures, as that note does not occur in the tune.

There is a black-letter ballad of *c.*1683 that bears a considerable resemblance to the form and ideas in 'The Lowlands of Holland' and may have been the inspiration for an early form of it. It is titled 'The Seaman's Sorrowful Bride'; the language is rather flowery. It begins:

My love is on the brackish sea and I am on this side
'Twould break a poor young creature's heart that lately was a bride
That lately was a joyful bride so pleasant to the eye
But Holland's land doth me withstand and part my love and I.

There is a transcription in *Roxburghe* VI, 444, and facsimiles of two editions in the Pepys collection can be seen at the University of California website: Pepys 3.58v and 4.193, the latter by J Deacon, at the Angel in Guiltspur-street without Newgate. Logan (*Pedlar's Pack*, 22) conjectures 'that its original source emanated from some incident connected with the Earl of Leicester's investment of the Low Countries or the wars of the Palatinate during the time of James I, and the subsequent progresses there of people from England and Scotland.'

Child 92, 'Bonny Bee Hom', shares some lines, and has sometimes – perhaps on quite slender grounds – been considered a relative; Child included a short version of 'Lowlands' from David Herd's *Scottish Songs* (1776, II, 2) in his notes (II, 317–8) and Bronson (II, 418–427) prints a number of examples as an appendix to Child 92, having no tune for 'Bee Hom' itself. A longer text, with tune, appeared in *SMM* II, 1788, number 115.

That it has existed long in oral tradition in most parts of the English-speaking world is indisputable. For this very reason it would be difficult, without further evidence, to pinpoint its origins. Pitts printed at least three markedly different slip versions during his career, and later in the nineteenth century the Dundee Poet's Box printed two variations. Evans of London shared a version with Pitts, and Pitts' successors also printed it. Widely different forms were also issued in Worcester, Birmingham, Manchester, Newcastle, Edinburgh and Cork. For examples, see Bodleian, Harding B 25(524): 'A new song, called The Distressed Sailor' (Angus of Newcastle); Harding B 11(2258) and Firth c.26(201): 'Lowlands of Holland' (Pitts, Pearson of Manchester); Harding B 11(419) and Firth c.12(421): 'Low Lands of Holland' (Such, Sefton of Manchester); Firth c.12(215) and Harding B 17(183b): 'The Maiden's Complaint for the Loss of her Sailor' (Pitts and Evans).

With this wide range of print sources available over a long period it is not surprising that oral versions are widespread and very varied. Southern English versions seem to derive variously from 'Lowlands of Holland' broadsides, which begin 'The night that I was married' or 'Last Easter I was married' and from 'Maiden's Complaint' forms, which begin 'As I walked out one May morning'. The rest of the narrative is much the same, though Holland is not mentioned in the latter; and in the former it has often acquired exotic characteristics such as sugar cane, which might suggest, as James Reeves remarked (*Everlasting Circle*, 180–2) that the earlier 'Holland' had become confused with 'New Holland' (the former name for Australia), and by extension with the Dutch East Indies.

We don't have William Bone's text, so Stephen Phillimore's, a 'Maiden's Complaint' version, has been used instead. His verse 5 has been moved into third place here, where it fits more comfortably into the narrative. In verse 2, he sang 'gallian(t) ship'; in verse 1, 'the chambers to behold' was presumably a mis-remembering of 'a charmer to behold', as in the 'Maiden's Complaint'. Mr Bone's tune was a 'Lazarus' variant; there is some structural similarity in Mr Phillimore's tune, but Bone's is far more striking.

Mr Bone's tune presented some difficulty; and not just for poor Charles Gamblin. The MS notation, as checked by Guyer, is in 3/4. When it was printed in the *FSJ* (III (13) 1909, 307) it had been re-noted by Vaughan Williams without time signature, but effectively in a mixture of 3/4, 5/8 and 2/4. The *Marrow Bones* notation, however, is in a compound of 5/4, 6/4 and 4/4, with most of the note durations doubled. Additionally, there was an error in bar 14: either this ought to have been shown as 4/4 instead of the implied 5/4, or else all five notes should have been crotchets with the 3rd and 4th tied. We have not so far established where the amended notation came from, even with the help of Frank Purslow, who suggested the second option for correction; so we have compromised by including both possible readings. The 6/4 bars are changed to a more appropriate 3/2. RVW's notation is included for comparison. His beaming is modified for the sake of clarity, but we have followed him in omitting time signatures.

There seem to be no recordings currently available from English tradition, but a Scottish version can be heard on Kyloe Records Kyloe 107, *Hamish Henderson Collects* (Bella Higgins, Perthshire), and an Irish one on Topic TSCD652, *My Ship Shall Sail the Ocean* (Paddy Tunney, Fermanagh).

MARROW-BONES

Roud 183 Laws Q2

This very popular comic song is no doubt much older than the few surviving early nineteenth-century printings. An 1818 Edinburgh garland contains an eleven-stanza version remarkably close to an oral version collected by James Telfer in Northumberland, *c.*1840 (See Harker, 336). The only other extant stall copy is a Pitts ten-stanza version in the Madden Collection, which sets the scene in Yorkshire. Many versions simply say 'our town' as in the Edinburgh print; which, incidentally, is in Standard English. Ireland is the next most popular setting, followed by Yorkshire and Kelso, but it can vary considerably; as one would expect from a song so widespread all over the English-speaking world. Scottish versions ('The Wily Auld Carle' or 'The Wife of Kelso') usually have marble(s) as the blinding agent instead of marrow-bones. It would seem reasonable to suggest that 'marbles' is a corruption of 'marrow bones'.

The song was rewritten as early as the late eighteenth century. Evans printed a pseudo-Scottish song 'The Scolding Wife', which has the same story but lacks the blinding motif. Also lacking this motif was John Sinclair's rewrite for the supper rooms, 'Johnny Sands' *c.*1840 (Roud 184), which became almost as popular as 'Marrow-Bones' and was published on music sheets on both sides of the Atlantic. There are several broadside examples at the Bodleian Library website, while sheet music of 1842 can be seen online at the Lester Levy Collection of Sheet Music.

John Pomery called his song 'The Jealous Old Woman'. In his verse 4, the old man ('a crafty old blade') wasn't taking any chances that the recipe might work:

He took up these two marrow-bones and dashed 'em on the floor.

We haven't yet established where the line substituted here came from, or the whole of our verse 5, in place of which Mr Pomery sang, a little puzzlingly:

Good Lord! How she did shriek and loud for mercy cry
Thou'st killed two of my dearest sons, what will become of me?

He also sang a further two verses at the end; as Henry Hammond noted, those actually came from a completely different song, 'The Man of Dover' (Roud 665), which was also in his repertoire:

So come all you jealous husbands wherever you may be
You never mind the women's work or cuckold you shall be.

For mine I have cuckold for seven long years or more
And now she's 'bliged to leave it o'er for her backside is sore.

Recordings from tradition can be heard on Topic TSCD656, *Tonight I'll Make You My Bride* (Jimmy Knights, Suffolk) and TSCD518D, *The Road from Connemara* (Joe Heaney, Galway); and on Musical Traditions MTCD329–0, *The Hardy Sons of Dan* (Red Mick McDermott, Fermanagh).

THE MILLER'S THREE SONS

Roud 138 Laws Q21

Tune noted by Duncan Hume.

'The Miller's Advice to his Three Sons on taking of Toll' appears on a broadside printed *c.*1730 in Aldermary Church Yard, London. This was reproduced in *Roxburghe* VII, 611–2, and an edition of the same period by Dicey and Marshall can be seen at Bodleian, Harding B 5(7) together with another without imprint, Douce Ballads 4(44). Considering that the song apparently did not appear on any broadsides after the mid-eighteenth century, it is remarkably widespread and intact. This can surely be put down to its repetitive structure and its strong dig at one of the most influential and distrusted trades of previous centuries. Millers ranked high in the village pecking order, and feature prominently in popular tradition as lechers and swindlers. The song was widespread in England and occurred in Scotland and Canada, but it was amazingly popular in the USA in the last two centuries, especially in the southern Appalachians where Sharp collected.

Hume noted only the first verse from Dr Graham, and the rest here seems to have been adapted from print sources; perhaps from the text printed in Dixon-Bell, 'The Miller and His Sons', which is also in J Collingwood Bruce and John Stokoe, *Northumbrian Minstrelsy* (Newcastle-upon-Tyne: Society of Antiquaries of Newcastle-upon-Tyne, 1882; repr. Felinfach: Llanerch, 1998), set to a tune which is clearly related to Dr Graham's. Another close relative is used in Scotland for 'The Merchant's Son and the Beggar Wench' (Roud 2153). A recording from tradition can be heard on Topic TSCD664, *Troubles They Are But Few* (Jumbo Brightwell, Suffolk: 'The Derby Miller'.)

MY BONNY, BONNY BOY

Roud 293

Tune noted by Guyer. Dorian/Lydian/Ionian, no 6th. Bb removed from key signature, as that note does not occur in the tune.

For background notes, see 'The Grey Hawk'. This is the woman's form of the song, sung here by the prolific George Blake. 'I once loved' is the usual beginning, but Mr Blake actually sang 'I lovèd'. Despite Simpson's comment that traditional survivals of 'Cupid's Trepan' use unrelated melodies, there does seem to be a faint echo of the old tune here. A recording from tradition – to a different melody – can be heard on Musical Traditions MTCD308, *Ythanside* (Daisy Chapman, Aberdeenshire).

MY CHARMING MOLLY, O

Roud 1605 and 2168

Tune noted by Hume. Dorian, no 6th. Bb removed from key signature, as that note does not occur in the tune.

Dr Graham's version is but a fragment of the seven double stanzas and chorus printed as 'Irish Molly O' on nineteenth-century broadsides. Pitts is the earliest, with a couple more London printings, a couple from Yorkshire and some later Glasgow and Edinburgh editions. It appears in several Irish broadside collection books and in 'Irish' songsters published in the USA. Not often collected in England or Ireland, it was much more popular in Scotland (the Greig-Duncan collection has 12 versions) and has turned up in Florida. For broadside examples, see Bodleian, Harding B 11(1787): Pitts; Harding B 11(4209): Such; Harding B 11(2121): Forth of Pocklington; and others without imprint. Two editions by James Kay of Glasgow can be seen at the National Library of Scotland website: shelfmarks L.C.178. A.2(256) and L.C.1270(006).

The broadside also inspired an answer in which Molly and William are parting on the shore before he sets sail. This was printed in London, York, Derby and Preston. See, for example, Firth b.26(167): J Paul of London, 'William of a Man of War' and Firth c.13(305): Harkness of Preston, 'Irish William'.

Dr Graham's text was slight:

Of all the charming girls about that I do chance to know
Ther're none half so pretty as my charming Molly, o.

She is young, she is beautiful...
Oh the only one entices me is charming Molly, o.
The flowers they will wither and their beauty fade away...

Of the rest of the *Marrow Bones* text, our second verse seems to have been reconstructed from a rather more full set noted from Henry King at Lyndhurst in May 1906 (H287):

Come all you pretty fair maids and a warning take by me
Never to build your nest on the top of any tree
For the green leaves they will wither and the roots they will decay
And the beauty of a fair maid how soon 'twill fade away.

This is much as in the broadsides, though of course the verse is a traditional 'floater' and occurs in many other songs. Since the broadsides have an unhappy ending, the final verse here is a puzzle; perhaps it was suggested by a single verse noted from Mrs Maria Etheridge at Southampton in June 1906 (H424), in which some lines have wandered in from 'Married Next Monday Morning' (Roud 579) or a similar song:

The leaves on the trees they will wither
And the birds in the air they will sing
And tomorrow I'm going to get married
And then you will hear the bells ring.

Dr Graham's tune has been re-ordered to accommodate the additional lines of text, thus:

Tune, line 1: as original line 1, with the final note in bar 4 dropped from D to A (as in original bar 7).
Lines 2, 3 and 4: as original.
Line 5: as original line 1.
Line 6: as original line 2.

The tune 'Irish Molly O' was named for several other broadside songs, but that may have been rather different from Dr Graham's, which however is a close relative of 'Irish Molly O' in O'Neill's *Irish Music*, 1915, Number 91, page 51.

NELLY THE MILKMAID

Roud 1606

Dorian with inflexion of 6th.

The earliest dated broadside copy is from Robertson of Glasgow, 1806. The song was printed by Pitts and Catnach and their followers, and later on at Horncastle, Manchester, Glasgow, Edinburgh and Dublin. Pitts' title was 'The Milk Maid got with Child at the Wake' and subsequent titles were either a shortening of this or 'Coming Home from the Wake'. Most of the London versions have Pitts' eight stanzas with no chorus. Disley printed six stanzas and suggested the multipurpose 'derry down' refrain. Most of the provincial printers followed this version. For broadside editions, see Bodleian, Firth b.34(178): Such; Firth b.33(47): Thornton of Kenilworth; and Harding B 40(3): probably Nugent of Dublin. The poet John Clare, incidentally, based his 'Dollys Mistake; or, the Ways of the Wake' (1820) on this song.

Marina Russell's opening words 'Nelly was a...' may have been influenced by the minstrel song of *c.*1850, 'Nelly was a Lady'. She had only two verses, as follows:

Nelly was a milkmaid fair and gay
Always took delight with young Roger to lay.
She grew stout at the heart and big at the waist
She thought upon the kissing coming home from the wake.

When five months was over and four months was gone
Nelly she brought forth a fine, lovely son.
I will name it, said she, I will name it for his sake
And call it 'Young Roger coming home from the wake'.

The *Marrow Bones* text is collated from this and Harry Cox's version, with some added touches from broadside copies. The Cox set (with a very different tune) can be heard on Topic TSCD512D, *The Bonny Labouring Boy*. The only other English version we know of is an unpublished one noted by Cecil Sharp from William Pratley in Oxfordshire, 1911. It has turned up in Aberdeenshire and Ulster, and a little more often in Canada and the USA (where the unfortunate infant is sometimes instead christened 'Shoot the Cat'; see the website of the Max Hunter Folk Song Collection at http://maxhunter.missouristate.edu/). A bawdy version, 'Young Roger of Kildare', survives as a rugby song.

NIGHTINGALES SING

Roud 140 Laws P14

Aeolian.

A ballad titled 'The Souldier and His Knapsack' was entered in the Stationers' Register in November 1639 and it is likely that this was an early appearance of 'The Nightingale's Song; or The Souldier's Rare Musick, and Maid's Recreation', of which two seventeenth-century printings survive. The edition by Wright, Clark, Thackeray and Passenger (early 1680s) is transcribed in *Roxburghe* VIII, clxx–clxi, and can be seen online at Pepys Ballads 4.41; there is also a damaged copy at Bodleian, 4o Rawl. 566(67). A slightly later copy by W Onley is at Bodleian, Douce Ballads 2(166b). The tune named is 'No, no, not I; Or, Peggy and the Souldier'. Richard Climsall, who appears to have been the author, has also been credited with 'The Souldier and Peggy' (Roud 907 Laws P13) and with a precursor of 'The Baffled Knight' (Roud 11, Child 112), 'The Politick Maid'. Climsall almost rivals Martin Parker when it comes to authorship of seventeenth-century predecessors of what we now call folk songs.

It is difficult to conceive that Disley's five-stanza 'Bold Grenadier' of *c*.1860 could have been composed directly from the sixteen-stanza seventeenth-century broadside ballad; it seems more likely to have been taken from oral tradition. It is also hard to believe that there wasn't at least one intermediate printing during the eighteenth century; but other ballads have persisted in oral tradition for more than two centuries with no apparent help from print. This version was also printed in Hull by William Forth (*c*.1870) and Willey of Cheltenham, and there is another without imprint (see Bodleian, Harding B 11(457)). While many of the oral forms widespread in England and America are based on the nineteenth-century redaction, a substantial number, particularly in America, have extra stanzas found only in the seventeenth-century broadside, even over and above the last two in William Bartlett's version.

'Perhaps a "Green Bushes" tune', wrote Henry Hammond; but note also the similarity of Mr Bartlett's melody to that of 'The Boys of Kilkenny', *q.v.* Recordings from tradition can be heard on Veteran VTC9CD, *Uncle Tom Cobleigh and All* (Charlie Pitman, Cornwall); Veteran VT153CD, *Romany Roots* (Vic Legg, Cornwall); and Musical Traditions MTCD317–8, *Chainmaker* (George Dunn, Warwickshire).

THE NOBLEMAN'S WEDDING

Roud 567 Laws P31

Few broadside editions of this ballad have survived. The earliest, 'The Wedding', printed by J Johnson of York in the early nineteenth century (York Publications, BL 286, transcribed in Emily Lyle, *Andrew Crawfurd's Collection of Ballads and Songs*, Edinburgh: Scottish Text Society, I, 1975, 235–6), has eight stanzas and shows signs of having been taken from oral tradition. The variety between versions and the fact that it is widespread point to eighteenth-century origins or earlier. The Glasgow Poet's Box printed a nine-stanza version, 'The Effect of Neglected Love', in 1852, set to the air 'It Stings to the Heart'. An Irish version, 'The Strange and Sorrowful Ballad of the Nobleman's Wedding', was printed in eight stanzas by Birmingham of Dublin in the 1860s.

Green willow as a signifier of lost or unrequited love occurs in popular song as least as far back as the sixteenth century, and a whole series of songs mentioning it appeared on broadsides in the early nineteenth; overlaps between them, and the occurrence in them of 'floating' verses, show that these were at least in part based on material already circulating in oral tradition. Mrs Crawford's final verse is fairly unusual in versions of 'The Nobleman's Wedding', though essentials of the two parts of it occur in, respectively, 'Green Willow' (and other titles; for two distinct forms, see Bodleian, Firth c.18(133) and Harding B 25(2061); and Harding B 11(1433) and Harding B 11(1432)) and 'The Willow-Will' (St Bride's Printing Library, S851):

It's all round my cap I will wear a green willow
It's all round my cap for a twelvemonth and a day
If anyone should ask you the reason why I wear it
O tell them I've been slighted by my truelove so gay.

and

If any young man can say he loves me,
Let him come and speak it now
This green garland don't become me
Tho' I'm forc'd to wear it now.

The former seems to have originated as a conflation of the final two verses of Scottish versions. 'Green Willow' was famously parodied in John Hansell and John Valentine's 'costermonger' song of *c.*1834, 'All Round my Hat' (Harding B 11(38): Pitts, and other editions; and see sheet music at the Lester Levy Collection, Box 046 Item 008). Examples of all these have survived in oral tradition, and are grouped with our song as Roud 567. The parody gave rise to further parodies, but most of those are long forgotten.

In verse 1, lines 3 and 4, Mrs Crawford sang:

As soon as she began for to think on some other
The farmer her own lovyer still runs in her mind.

In verse 4, line 1, she sang 'pillow' rather than 'bosom', and verse 7 ended 'He went and he found that his new bride was dead.' Verse 9, line 3, was 'And if this here willow it should not become me'. Verses 3, 5 and 8 are introduced from elsewhere. The first is common in oral versions, while 5 and 8 are rare; perhaps they have been adapted from an unprovenanced broadside text quoted by Padraic Colum in *Broadsheet Ballads* (Dublin; London: Maunsel, 1913) and *Anthology of Irish Verse*, 1922. Mrs Crawford's tune is related to the melody Sharp got from Lucy White at Hambridge in 1904, and to Irish 'Nobleman's Wedding' tunes in Petrie (numbers 491–495).

'The Nobleman's Wedding' itself has only been found occasionally in oral tradition in England, chiefly around the south coast. It was, however, much more popular in Scotland, was found in Ireland (mainly in the north), and was fairly widespread in the USA and Canada. Recordings from tradition can be heard on Musical Traditions MTCD308, *Ythanside* (Daisy Chapman, Aberdeenshire); and on Topic TSCD656, *Tonight I'll Make You My Bride* (Eddie Butcher, Derry) and TSCD515, *From the Heart of the Tradition* (Sheila Stewart, Perthshire).

No, Sir, No

Roud 146

Tunes: (1) Ionian. (2) Dorian. C♯ added to key signature, as all instances of C were sharpened.

One of our more interesting 'ancient' folk songs which, in its present form, does not appear on broadsides; though its general theme and ideas can be traced back at least to the early days of popular print. The form is usually a dialogue in which the man presses his suit and the woman gives a negative response at the end of each stanza. He then cleverly changes tack and presents his case in such a way that her obstinate repeated denial becomes a double negative, thus giving consent.

One such is 'The Denying Lady' of 1670–97 (Pepys 5.248). The refrain is similar to our version: 'Her answer it still was no'. Even closer to the modern text is 'The Dumb Lady; or, No, no not I I'le Answer' (1672–95; Pepys 3.128, *Roxburghe* VI, 352, and Bodleian, Douce Ballads 1(65b)); the refrain this time is 'Still she answer'd no not I'. The basic pattern continued along several lines into the nineteenth century: 'No Tom, No' in the Madden Collection, although a dialogue between Tom and Dolly, has a refrain remarkably close to the 'Oh, No, John' versions of 'No, Sir, No'.

The modern oral form has been found mainly in the southern English counties, but versions have also turned up in Herefordshire and Lancashire. There are about as many US versions as there are English, but they tend to have fewer stanzas. The stock of stanzas amounts to nine that are found regularly: the most complete set, of seven, is in the Herefordshire version recorded by Peter Kennedy from Emily Bishop in 1952 (*Folksongs of Britain and Ireland*, London: Cassell, 1975; repr. Oak Publications, 1984; 315), which even then lacks the first two stanzas of the general stock.

Our text here is a compilation; the second verse is actually from a different song, 'Madam, Madam' (Roud 542) which has also become crossed with 'No, Sir, No' in a Florida version. Sharp also made a composite of the two songs in *Folk Songs from Somerset* (Series 4, 46) and this, having been much reprinted, has caused people to confuse these two quite separate songs ever since. What seems to have happened here is that John Greening knew a few verses of both songs but sang them to the same tune. Our first two verses are his, with Mrs Bowring's chorus, while verses 4–7 are from Mrs Bowring with a few amendments: in verse 7 line 3, for example, she sang 'sounder' rather than 'sweeter'. That verse seems to be unique to her version, though a lot of singers have since adopted it. Verse 3 is not to be found in the Hammond MSS; the nearest form we know of was noted by Cecil Sharp from James Beale at Warehorne, Kent, in 1908:

> My husband he was a Spanish captain
> He went to sea about three months ago
> And the very last time we kissed and parted
> He always told me to answer No.

Mrs Bowring's tune as given here is simplified; she sang many alternative notes in the course of her song. An example from tradition – to a different tune – can be heard on Topic TSCD511, *Now is the Time for Fishing* (Sam Larner, Norfolk).

NOTHING AT ALL

Roud 1184

Ever since the early seventeenth century, broadside hacks rather surprisingly have taken 'nothing' as one of their more popular subjects. This scarce song was one of the earliest issued on broadsides by Bebbington of Manchester; the only copy is number 43 in the Axon Ballad Collection at Chetham's Library, Manchester. The text is much the same as Robert Barratt's but it has a full chorus of 'Derry, down, down, down. Derry, down, high derry down.' A further, unprovenanced broadside edition (beginning 'Now since I have nothing to do' and without chorus, but sharing verses with ours) can be seen at Bodleian, Harding B 26(1): 'A new song about nothing at all'. Likely the song is late eighteenth century; the British Library catalogue lists a music sheet by John Rice of Dublin, *c.*1780, 'Now since I have Nothing to do. The admird Song of Nothing at all.'

Beside Mr Barratt's version, there are two texts in Harker 352–353; and Sharp got a set in Virginia, 1918 (*Folk Words* p 3138 / *Folk Tunes* p 4451). Mr Barratt's chorus actually went 'And sing fol the dol diddle the dee'; the form given here seems to have been an inadvertent editorial substitution. In verse 3, he sang 'For knowledge brings sorrow, you see'; 'money' is editorial. Of the tune, Frank Purslow wrote: 'This appears to be an adaptation of a dance tune which might have been in 9/8 time'.

OLD GREY BEARD A-WAGGING

Roud 362

Tune noted by Guyer.

Another of those rare and intriguing creatures, the widespread orally transmitted songs with no known stall copies to rely on. Presumably it owes its widespread appeal to its humour, its very simple structure and its suitability for modification and enlargement. It appears in Scotland in two forms. The earlier, 'The Carle He Came o'er the Craft', was first printed in Allan Ramsay's *Tea-Table Miscellany* (1724–27), and shortly thereafter, as 'The Young Lass Contra Auld Man', in John Watts' *Musical Miscellany* (London: III, 1730); it was reprinted in other Scottish collections of the period; and later on again in England (*Universal Songster* II, 247). Although it is undoubtedly related to our widespread oral version, it only has the first stanza in common and the structure is different. This version may have had some oral currency in earlier centuries but there is little evidence of this.

As early as 1803 the more popular version appeared in *SMM* V, number 416, along with its cousin above (II, number 134). Robert Ford's *Vagabond Songs & Ballads of Scotland* (Paisley: Gardner, 1899–1901) also prints both. A Northumbrian version of *c.*1850, 'There Was an Old Man Came Over the Lea', was printed in Dixon-Bell, Ballad LXXXIII. Considering the earliest examples came from Scotland it is surprisingly scarce there. England shows a scattering of versions; mainly in the south, though it has also been found in Yorkshire and Northumberland. In Canada a few versions have turned up in Nova Scotia, but amazingly it has been collected in almost every state of the USA.

Guyer's notation shows Henry Purkiss as singing 'And his old grey *head* went nodding' throughout, but this appears in the typescript transcription as 'And his old grey beard went nodding'. Mr Purkiss' tune is not greatly changed from the *SMM* version of a century before. Recordings from tradition can be heard on Veteran VTC5CD, *When the Wind Blows* (Mabs Hall, Sussex: 'Old Grey Noddle') and Musical Traditions MTCD335–6, *In Memory of Lizzie Higgins* (Lizzie Higgins, Aberdeenshire: 'Dottered Auld Carle').

AN OLD MAN CAME COURTING ME

Roud 210

Tune noted by Gamblin.

Although a form of this song, 'Scant of Love, Want of Love', appears in David Herd's *Ancient and Modern Scottish Songs, Heroic Ballads etc.* (edition of 1869, appendix 'containing the pieces substituted in the edition of 1791 for those omitted in the edition of 1776', 349), most oral versions seem to derive from the broadside printed by Harkness of Preston in the mid-nineteenth century (see Bodleian, Harding B 11(2627)). 'Never Maids Wed an Old Man' has an interleaved 'derry down' refrain, and this, or variations upon it, occurs in most traditional forms. Though very similar in many ways to the previous song, this one is very scarce in the USA and Canada, with single versions found in Utah, Kentucky and Ontario. Only a handful of examples have turned up in Scotland and Ireland, but it has been widely dispersed and relatively common in England.

Our first verse is adapted from another version (H997) sung by Mrs Hopkins of Axford:

> An old man came courting me
> Heigh down, oh down …
> An old man came courting me
> Oh for to ruin me
> Likes of my heart never wed an old man.

It should be noted that 'kiss' is frequently used euphemistically in folk song. The versions most often heard today derive from those of Sam Larner (Norfolk) and Jeannie Robertson (Aberdeenshire); these can be heard on, respectively, Topic TSCD511, *Now is the Time for Fishing*, and TSCD651, *Come Let Us Buy the Licence*. Both tunes, though they sound very different at first hearing, are recognisably related to each other and to Mrs Davey's melody.

ONE MAN SHALL SHEAR MY WETHERS

Roud 143

Ionian, no 7th.

Along with its better known version, 'Mowing Down the Meadow', this cumulative song seems to have served a dual purpose as an accompaniment for both working and drinking: 'often called for at the harvest-homes and other farm feasts', as Alfred Williams put it. It was pressed into service as a marching song during the Great War, and the occasional examples found in Australia, the USA and Canada were probably taken there by ex-servicemen. As 'One Man Went to Mow' it later became universally known as a children's and campfire song, the tune of which was used by Lonnie Donegan for his 'My Old Man's a Dustman', beside carrying the rugby song 'If I were the Marrying Kind'. In spite of that last association, it doesn't seem especially likely that, as James Reeves hinted (*Everlasting Circle*, 200–1) there was any particular erotic subtext in the original song, however common mowing may have been as a sexual metaphor.

Gardiner and the Hammonds found examples of both forms of the song. There is no clear record of how Mrs Stone dealt with the repeats, but a similar version from William Brown (D587) of Nether Compton, Dorset, sung to a related tune, went up to twelve men (counting backwards instead of forwards as here) and then back down to one. Mr Wyatt (Wt913) of Marlborough, Wiltshire, on the other hand, went all the way up to forty. His tune was quite different. Mrs Stone sang 'bind' rather than 'gather', and pronounced 'wool' in the old way: ''ool'. A recording from tradition of the 'mowing' form can be heard on Musical Traditions MTCD304, *Come Hand to Me the Glass* (George Townsend, Suffolk).

For more on cumulative and forfeit songs, see *FSJ* V (20) 1916, 277–296.

THE PENNY WAGER

Roud 393

Tune noted by Guyer.

Though the earliest surviving broadside editions date from about 1790, the content suggests that the song may be older. Evans printed it first, followed by Pitts and Catnach in London and Kendrew in York; all under the title 'Adventures of a Penny', with a standard eight stanzas and chorus. For the Pitts edition, see Bodleian, Harding B 16(2b), and two other copies. It has been found in oral currency, under a variety of names, all over the south of England; and isolated examples have turned up in Clare, Virginia, New Hampshire and Australia.

William Tod actually sang the two lines of the chorus the other way about; here they have been restored to their usual order. He began verse 4 thus:

I took up the dice and I threw them a maze
It was my good fortune for to raise...

His final verse ended: 'She said, One kiss, love, and then box away.' His tune is noticeably similar to Charles Gamblin's 'Devil and the Farmer's Wife', *q.v.* Recordings from tradition can be heard on Musical Traditions MTCD317–8, *Chainmaker* and Topic TSCD663, *They Ordered Their Pints of Beer* (George Dunn, Warwickshire: 'Little Grey 'Oss'); and on Topic TSCD661, *My Father's the King of the Gypsies* (Levi Smith, Surrey: 'One Penny').

THE PLOUGHBOY'S DREAM

Roud 1545

Tune noted by Gamblin. Mixolydian.

These verses were written by the Revd William Mason (1725–1797), a friend of the writers Thomas Gray and Horace Walpole. They were first published by John Marshall at 17 Queen Street, Cheapside, *c.*1785, as part of the *Cheap Repository for Moral and Religious Tracts* series, which was initiated by Hannah More (1745–1833) and Henry Thornton. They were intended as 'improving' antidotes to the profane broadside and chapbook market, and were deliberately produced and sold in the same fashion. Most of the initial songs (sometimes set to popular tunes of the day) were written by Hannah More herself; she later worked with various lady assistants and their output was influential at the time, though such effusions as 'The Execution of Wild Robert' or 'The Riot, or half a loaf is better than no bread' are long forgotten. For further details, see J S Bratton, *The Victorian Popular Ballad* (London: MacMillan, 1975, 138–141).

For copies of the Marshall print, see Bodleian, Harding B 7(44) and Johnson Ballads fol. 184A: 'The Plow-Boy's Dream'. The song was reprinted, with the eight stanzas split into sixteen quatrains, by Catnach and his successors, among others. See, for example, Johnson Ballads 2083: 'The Plough-Boy's Dream' (M W Carrall, York, *c.*1827) and Harding B 11(3032): 'The Ploughboy's Dream' (W S Fortey, London, between 1858 and 1885).

Mr Wigg had forgotten some lines, and our text here is an arrangement into verses of what he recalled. Verse 2, line 2 seems to be editorial, as does the final part of verse 5, line 4, where he actually sang 'Blue flames broke forth and in those flames dived his anter shot', remarking that 'this ought to mean Satan'. It's worth noting that Mr Wigg called the second horse Ball (a common name for horses; see also notes to 'The Trooper's Horse'), not Belle; and that this is confirmed by the broadside text. Singers may like to know that 'it's better far than gold' in verse 4, line 2, is 'or better for them go' in the broadsides.

The song hasn't lasted particularly well in tradition. Beside Mr Wigg's version, sung to a variant of the widespread 'Lazarus' tune (very close to the one William Bolton used for 'Rounding the Horn'; see *CEFS*, 58) it has turned up in Aberdeenshire and Orkney; but most famously in Forest Green, Ockley, Surrey, where Vaughan Williams noted a set in 1903 from a Mr Garman, sung to a tune which was later used in *The English Hymnal* for 'O Little Town of Bethlehem'.

POLLY VAUGHAN

Roud 166 Laws O56

Tune noted by Gamblin. Aeolian.

Until recently it was generally thought that the first print reference to this popular song was in Robert Jamieson, *Popular Ballads and Songs, from Tradition, Manuscripts, and Scarce Editions; with Translations of Similar Pieces from the Ancient Danish Language, and a few Originals by the Editor* (Edinburgh: Archibald Constable, I, 1806, 193–199) where he quotes an incomplete text from a maidservant in Aberdeen, noting that he himself had heard a version of it in childhood (around 1785–6, in Morayshire). Although deeply impressed by it as a child, he writes of it disparagingly; though rather in the way of one who 'doth protest too much'; a point which later commentators seem to have missed.

New information has recently come to light. A garland titled 'My Friend and Pitcher' (Lillenhall Library, Belfast, Pamphlet Book 1031, item [9]) printed in 1797, includes a text as 'The Youths Grievance; or, the Downfall of Molly Bawn.' It names the hero as 'Rawlings' and the heroine as Molly Bawn Lowry, 'the Beauty of Ulster and the Star of Kilwarning', adding that she was born and well educated in Lurgan. The same essential details occur on a later songsheet printed by Conolly of Galway, *c.*1820 (National Library of Ireland LO Song

Books, Galway, n.d. (3)). Hugh Shields, 'Some Songs and Ballads in use in the Province of Ulster ... 1845' (*Ulster Folklife* 17, 1971, 3–24) describes an MS example from Kilwarlin near Hillsborough, County Down (NLI MS 490) which names the protagonists as James Reynolds and Molly Bann Lavery, 'the Pride of the North and the Flower of Kilwarlin', born in Lisburn and educated in Lurgan. He notes that the surnames are local, the Laverys being Catholics and the Reynoldses Protestants.

The *Bottle and Frien'ds* [sic] *Garland*, printed *c.*1780 in Newcastle (British Library 11621.c.3.(4.)), includes 'A Song, call'd Molly Bawn' which begins in the same way as some later broadsides but shows signs of having been taken from an oral source. It names the locale as 'Kiln-wan' and the hero as Johnny Wrangle. The text is further from the presumed original form than are the known Ulster examples, but it is the earliest so far identified, and goes some way to explaining why Jamieson thought the song a modern English stall ballad.

Broadside versions, differing quite widely, were issued by a number of printers during the nineteenth century; for examples, see Bodleian, 2806 b.11(21): Pitts, 'Molly Whan'; Harding B 17(197b): 'Molly Whan' (no imprint); 2806 c.18(209): Haly of Cork, 'Molly Bawn'; 2806 c.15(49): Nugent of Dublin, 'An admired song called Young Molly Bawn'. Versions were also published in York, New York, and Boston.

Joyce (220) remarked that the song had been 'very popular in the midland and southern counties' of Ireland during the nineteenth century, adding 'it obviously commemorates a tragedy in real life.' Other commentators of a more romantic bent, however, seized on the ghostly apparition of the heroine at the end and decided that the whole song must be supernatural, Polly or Molly herself having being *actually in the form of a swan* (a fawn in some versions) rather than merely mistaken for one in poor light (see *FSJ* VII (26) 1922, 17–21). This theory reached its apotheosis when A L Lloyd wrote (*Folk Song in England*, 154–5) 'the modern-seeming ballad ... in fact reaches far back beyond the time of classical mythology ... [it] turns out to be connected with the fantasies of primitive hunting societies ...' (and more in the same vein.)

In fairness, a few oral versions do have Polly's ghost appearing at her lover's trial in the form of a swan, but these are late, rather confused examples, and English. It may be time to relegate those Celtic (or Norse) swan-maidens and enchanted deer to the folkloric background, and return instead to Joyce's opinion which, in view of the available evidence, is far more likely. A glance at American newspapers will confirm that it is still quite common for hunters to shoot people under the impression that they are game, and an incident in the Lurgan area in the first half of the eighteenth century may well have given rise to our song. It is possible that records of the time may eventually reveal more.

'A lover killing his mistress, a grey-haired old father, and a ghost', as Jamieson wrote, are quite enough to account for the song's great popularity in tradition. It has been found widely in Ireland, the south and east of England and the eastern USA, and has turned up in Canada and Australia; though it seems to have been forgotten in Scotland since Jamieson's time. 'Vaughan' ('Whan' in some versions) probably derives from the pronunciation of the aspirated form of the Irish 'bán' (anglicised as 'bawn'): 'bhán'.

Our text here is collated from various sources. Verses 2 and 3 are from Mrs Matthews and verse 4 is a combination of text from her and from William Bone, probably with additions from George Smith (H448: Fareham, Hampshire, July 1906). Verses 1 and 5 contain elements from all these, perhaps also with touches from Hammond D390 and D448 (J Handsford and Henry Way; both Bridport, Dorset, May 1906). A further version, H1330 (Albert Doe, Bartley, Hampshire, December 1908) doesn't seem to be involved; but of all these, his is the text that retains a reference to 'Kilwany'. The tune is William Bones', while the variations are from Mrs Matthews. In common with most melodies found with this song, it appears to be originally Irish, though changed rather by English singers. On the one hand it resembles 'Coola Shore', to which A P Graves set his 'My Love's an Arbutus', and which is found in America as 'Pretty Saro'; on the other it is reminiscent of the famous tune that Butterworth found in Norfolk, sung to 'The Banks of Green Willow'.

Recordings from tradition can be heard on Topic TSCD653, *O'er His Grave the Grass Grew Green* (Phoebe Smith, Suffolk); TSCD512D, *The Bonny Labouring Boy* (Harry Cox, Norfolk); TSCD656, *Tonight I'll Make You My Bride* (Packie Manus Byrne, Donegal); Musical Traditions MTCD305–6, *Put a Bit of Powder on it Father* (Walter Pardon, Norfolk); and on Musical Traditions MTCD329–0, *The Hardy Sons of Dan*, and Veteran VT134CD, *Linkin' o'er the Lea* (Maggie Murphy, Fermanagh).

See *English Dance and Song* 68 (3) autumn 2006 for the Bone and Matthews tunes, and, for further discussion, Jennifer J O'Connor, 'The Irish Origins and Variations of the Ballad "Molly Brown"' in *Canadian Journal for Traditional Music*, 14, 1986 (http://cjtm. icaap.org/content/14/v14art3.html).

THE POOR OLD COUPLE

Roud 491

Although this song is very much in the stall ballad idiom, we know of no broadside copies. There is a Scottish text, 'The Absent Farmer', in Peter Buchan's unpublished *Secret Songs of Silence* (*c.*1820), but the first print appearance seems to be in James Orchard Halliwell, *Popular Rhymes and Nursery Tales of England* (London: John Russell Smith, 1849; repr. London: Bodley Head, 1970, 264), where it is much as here, though there is no mention of any clandestine visit or of adultery. Baring-Gould (*Garland*, 100) gives a similar version, commenting: 'This song is sung by nurses and old women all through England. The story is derived from one of the Mediaeval Fabliaux, but one of the characteristic elements is omitted to suit it to the nursery.' He does not specify which of the many fabliaux he had in mind, but the full story (in some versions the old man falls from the tree, sometimes to his death; and sometimes with assistance from his wife) is not so very different from much that features in the works of Chaucer and his sources.

The text here is modified. In verse 3 lines 3 and 4, Mrs Seale sang:

He slipped in with the woman to lie
Oh what a good clerk was he...

Her fourth verse went:

The old man he returned at last
He found the doors and the windows fast
Oh what is the matter cried he...

Verses 4–7 here are introduced from elsewhere. Although Gardiner H1026 (William Burgess) has quite a full text, the syntax is very different; the version noted by Sharp from Henry Reed (Axbridge, 1908; see Reeves, *Idiom of the People* 174 and Karpeles II, 8–9), however, has verses almost identical to our 4–7, with an additional concluding stanza:

O I have been sick since you have been gone
My sickness was all for the want of a man.
Poor wife, said he. Poor cuckold, thought she.

Mr Reed's tune appears to be related to Mrs Seale's, which was barred slightly differently in the MS, where our bars 9 and 10 were combined into a single bar in 9/8, as were our bars 12 and 13. Apart from a couple of American examples, the song has only been found in oral currency in southern England and East Anglia. A recording from tradition can be heard on Veteran VTC1CD, *Stepping It Out: Traditional Folk Songs & Dances From England* (Manny Aldous, Suffolk: 'Cleverly Done Said He').

THE RAMBLING SOLDIER

Roud 21266

Tune noted by Gamblin. Mixolydian/Ionian, with inflexion of 7th.

Written by John Morgan, a writer for the broadside press who was active in the 1830s and 1840s, closely based on an older song, 'The Rambling Sailor' (Roud 518). Broadside copies mention 'the King', so presumably it was written some time prior to Victoria's accession in 1837. George Digweed, having learned the song during Victoria's reign, sang 'the Queen'. He also followed the broadsides in naming the soldier as 'Bill', though the original edition of *Marrow Bones* left this blank to encourage singers to insert the name of their choice.

Quite widely printed on broadsides, though not so often as its forerunner, of which the eighteenth-century edition by Angus of Newcastle may be the original. Pitts and Catnach issued it, along with their contemporaries and followers, plus the usual provincial printers up through Birmingham, Lancashire, Yorkshire and Durham to Edinburgh. It has six stanzas on all stall versions and varies very little. For examples, see, among others, Bodleian, Harding B 11(835): Pitts; Firth c.14(201): Such; Harding B 16(221a): Hill of London; Harding B 15(251b): Keys of Devonport; Harding B 20(143): Harkness of Preston; Harding B 11(3228): Fordyce of Newcastle; and Harding B 17(251a): Sanderson of Edinburgh. It also appeared in publications such as the American *Forget-Me-Not Songster*.

Unlike 'The Rambling Sailor', 'The Rambling Soldier' is very scarce in oral tradition. In addition to this one there is a Cornish version collected by Fred Hamer (*Garners Gay*, London: EFDS 1967, 74) and in the USA it has been found in Florida and Carolina. Some broadsides specify the 'Rambling Sailor' tune, and Mr Digweed's melody is recognisably a variant of this. Indeed, the tune and format have been well used: there is also 'The Rambling Miner' (Bodleian, Firth b.26(133) and others), 'The Rambling Comber' (Roud 1473), 'The Female Rambling Sailor' (Roud 17784) and 'The Gallant Soldier' (Roud 2496).

There are no available recordings from tradition of 'The Rambling Soldier', but 'The Rambling Sailor' can be heard on Topic TSCD662, *We've Received Orders to Sail* (Chris Willett, Kent, 1962) and on EFDSS CD002, *A Century of Song* (probably Peter Verrall, Sussex, 1907). The latter can also be heard at the British Library's *Collect Britain* website (http://www.collectbritain.co.uk/).

RAP-A-TAP-TAP

Roud 792

Tune noted by Balfour Gardiner.

Quite a scarce song; the oldest broadside version extant is 'Old Mother Flip Flop Against a Wash-Tub' with seven stanzas, the last of which runs:

> Come all my good companions we saw a flock of geese
> Come all my good companions we'll knock down six apiece
> For that is true my boys as I've heard many say
> I saw an old woman scrating [sic] her c--y just contray way.

There is no imprint, but it appears to be early nineteenth century.

Disley of London, Pearson of Manchester and Harkness of Preston printed a five-stanza version which corresponds with John Carter's text; which, noted Gardiner, was 'too broad to be sent in [to the Folk-Song Society]'. See Bodleian, Firth b.34(252): 'Rap a Tap, Tap' (Disley, illegible) and two others without imprint: 2806 c.13(159): 'My Mistress Came to the Door' and Firth b.34(162): 'My Mistress Came to the Door or A Rap, Tap, Tap'. Another song using the 'door-knocking' motif was 'The Chandler's Wife' (Roud 10265; and see Bodleian, Harding B 25(356)); this survives in the armed forces and among rugby players and is usually sung to the 'Lincolnshire Poacher' tune. A re-written version of it, 'The

Thing', was a surprise hit in 1950 on the RCA label for the American singer Phil Harris, who in later life was the voice of Baloo the Bear in Disney's film of *The Jungle Book*.

Note the resemblance of Mr Carter's tune to that of 'The Ups and Downs', *q.v.*, which has almost become 'The Lincolnshire Poacher' by the time it ends. Oral versions are just as scarce as broadsides. The Hammonds found it (also with a related tune) and it was popular in the East Anglian hotbeds of song in the mid-twentieth century. Examples from tradition can be heard on Topic TSCD655, *Come My Lads that Follow the Plough* and Musical Traditions MTCD301–2, *A Broadside* (Bob Hart, Suffolk, 1970 and 1969); and on Rounder ROUCD1839, *What Will Become of England* (Harry Cox, Norfolk, 1953).

ROGER'S COURTSHIP

Roud 575

Tune noted by Gamblin. Ionian, no 7th.

The earliest reference to this old comic song is in Gay's *Beggar's Opera*, Act III, Scene VIII, where the tune 'Now, Roger, I'll tell thee because thou'rt my son' is assigned to 'When a wife's in her pout'. It has all the hallmarks of a seventeenth-century piece. Although no version surviving has more than eight stanzas, when all versions are pieced together it appears that the original had at least twelve. William Chappell, responding to a query asking for further words in *Notes and Queries* in 1875, mentioned the *Beggar's Opera* reference and added that he had seen the song in a collection but couldn't recall where. Previous versions printed in *Notes and Queries* in 1871 were from *c.*1800. A seven-stanza version appears in *The Universal Songster*, 1826, II, 368, as 'Poor Bob'.

Our verse 4 is borrowed from a text in Williams, 171–2, 'Old Mother Hooligan'. Oral versions are widely distributed throughout Britain and Northern Ireland, but are not particularly common. Gardiner and the Hammonds noted a number of examples, and it has survived in several variants in the West Country, Lancashire and Aberdeenshire. An example from tradition can be heard, as 'Jan's Courtship', on Veteran VTC4CD, *Down in the Fields* (Archer Goode, Gloucestershire, learned from Sam Bennett of Warwickshire).

THE SAILOR DECEIVED

Roud 152 Laws M1

Aeolian.

'This three-verse fragment,' wrote Frank Purslow in the original edition, 'although complete in itself, is actually part of a much longer ballad.' That ballad has had a long and varied life, having been in continuous currency since *c.*1680 with, seemingly, little help from print. As 'The Seaman's complaint for his Unkind Mistress of Wapping' it was published by various London printers in the late seventeenth century and examples survive in several collections: Pepys 5.364 can be seen at http://emc.english.ucsb.edu/ballad_project/ and see also *Roxburghe Ballads*, VIII, 433.

The tune specified is 'I love you dearly, I love you well' (for two possibilities, see Simpson, 293–7) and there does seem to be a relationship with John Pomery's tune, which is also reminiscent of 'The Dark-Eyed Sailor' (Roud 256, Laws N35). The song family is extensive and varied, and cousins include 'The Croppy Boy', (Roud 1030, Laws J14) *q.v.*, and another song set early in the spring (as longer forms of 'The Sailor Deceived' often are), 'A Sailor's Life' (Roud 273, Laws K12).

The early broadside had fourteen stanzas, and ten of these, with a little shunting, survived in 'The Sailor Deceived' (see John Ashton, *Real Sailor Songs*, London: Leadenhall Press, 1891, 56) as printed by Bloomer of Birmingham, a copy of which is in Cecil Sharp's collection in the Vaughan Williams Memorial Library. Pitts printed an eleven-stanza version,

'The Disappointed Sailor', which added two new verses (see Roy Palmer, *Boxing the Compass*, 106–7, where an eleven-stanza text from Logan, *Pedlar's Pack*, is set to the second tune quoted by Simpson); and the first and fifth stanzas of the earliest version were the basis for a new ballad, 'The True-Hearted Sailor', printed by Mate of Dover *c*.1810.

Oral versions are widespread and popular in the English-speaking world. Most are very fragmented and have acquired new verses, particularly in America. Strangely, Pomery's first stanza only occurs elsewhere in the southern United States. In the American south, the ballad was remade into a cowboy song, 'The Trail to Mexico'. Examples from tradition can be heard on Veteran VTC5CD, *When the Wind Blows* (Norman Perks, Gloucestershire) and VT134CD, *Linkin' o'er the Lea* (Maggie Murphy, Fermanagh); Topic TSCD518D, *The Road from Connemara* (Joe Heaney, Galway) and TSCD665, *As Me and My Love Sat Courting* (Robert Cinnamond, Antrim).

SERIOUS TOM

Roud 1608

Tune noted by Gamblin.

Although the general subject was a popular one, this particular song appears to be a unique example, and we have not so far found any information about it. The structure of the tune suggests that it is fairly old; perhaps it was a tavern song or a product of the 'Glee Clubs' of the eighteenth century.

THE SHEEP SHEARING SONG

Roud 812

Dorian.

This song was composed, as 'The Sheep-Sheering Ballad', by John Barret[t] for Charles Johnson's comedy *The Country Lasses; or, the Custom of the Manor*, which was first staged at the Theatre Royal, Drury Lane in 1714. Johnson wrote the words and it was sung by the actor Mr Burkhead. Barrett was born *c*.1674 and studied with Dr John Blow (who also taught Henry Purcell), becoming a church organist and teacher of music at Christ's Hospital; some of his songs appear in the works of Thomas D'Urfey. Johnson (1679–1748) had been destined for the law, but fell victim to the lure of the stage; he also wrote *The Village Opera* (1729), an early attempt to cash in on the success of John Gay's *Beggar's Opera*. At one time he kept a tavern on Bow Street.

The play was revived periodically throughout the eighteenth century, and probably later. Our song appeared on at least one slip during that time; in the nineteenth it was printed by Evans, Pitts, Catnach and Hodges in London, and was also issued in Bristol, York and Manchester. See Bodleian, Firth b.25(209) (Evans: 'The sheep-shearers'); Harding B 11(2287) (Pitts: 'The sheep shearers'); Johnson Ballads fol. 16 (Catnach: 'The sheep-shearing'); and Harding B 11(2842) (Hodges: 'The sheep shearing').

The small number of oral versions on record were all found in the southern counties, and all in the first decade of the twentieth century; apart from one noted by the Revd John Broadwood around 1843. The tune remains close to Barrett's original. The second alternative note for 'June' here is editorial, the intention having been to avoid ending the phrase on the tonic.

SHEPHERD'S SONG

Roud 284

Aeolian, no 6th.

Quite common in the south of England in the early part of the twentieth century, the song persists; Gwilym Davies found several examples in the 1980s and '90s. No broadside editions are known, but the refrain 'stormy winds do blow' might suggest a possible connection with a seventeenth-century ballad in the same meter by Martin Parker, 'Neptune's Raging Fury: or The Gallant Seaman's Sufferings' (for which, see Bodleian, Douce Ballads 2(167b)), set to the tune 'When the Stormy Winds Do Blow'; certainly Frank Kidson thought so. However that may be, tunes found in tradition vary considerably. Some belong to the 'Lazarus' family, while others have more in common with 'The Bay of Biscay' (Roud 524 Laws K3). Whether any of these are related to the 'When the Stormy Winds Do Blow' tune is not easy to say; see Simpson, 768–9, for further detail.

　　Our tune is from William Cole; the text is a collation. Verse 1 is from Mr Cole, while verses 2 and 4 are from Benjamin Arnold (both edited) and verse 3 is from Moses Mills. Mr Arnold began our second verse:

> Come all you galliant shepherds that has got galliant tongues
> That do go out in the morning and never fear a storm...

　　Recordings from traditional singers can be heard on Veteran VTC7CD, *It was on a Market Day vol 2* (Bob Lewis, Sussex) and on Veteran VTD148CD, *A Shropshire Lad* and Topic TSCD670, *There is a Man Upon the Farm* (Fred Jordan, Shropshire). Fred Jordan seems to have learned his version from the collector Fred Hamer (who apparently got it from Lucy Broadwood's *English County Songs*, 1893) rather than directly from tradition, and Bob Lewis' text (recorded in 1989) is almost identical to the *Marrow Bones* collation; but both are sung in traditional styles.

THE SHOEMAKER'S KISS

Roud 3807

Our tune and interleaved refrain are from William Bartlett. He called his song 'Green as the Leaves are Green', and began it thus:

> There was an old woman lived in the west
> So green as the leaves are green, green, green, green
> So green as the leaves are green
> And she had ale and beer of the best
> So green as the leaves are green, green, green, green
> So green as the leaves are green.

　　'No opportunity of getting the rest of the words which were in part obscene', wrote Henry Hammond (notebook 6 number 147), adding in his MS 'The remainder was very coarse'. Some confusion has arisen due to the brevity of the text, which almost certainly belonged to 'The Trooper's Horse', *q.v.*, and to the similarity of the tune to that given with 'The Shoemaker's Kiss', noted from George Bowditch, whose version supplies the rest of our text. Although both songs open in a similar fashion, they do not belong together. Mr Bowditch began:

> There was an old woman lived down in the west
> Hey ho! and her name it was Nannye
> She had a fine daughter that never was kissed
> It was all in the morning so early.

He continued as here, though there are some editorial amendments. His verses 4–6 were:

Come in, pretty maiden, sit down by my side.
Good Lord, how he kissed her and caught her sweet lips.

When twenty long weeks they were all over and past
This little bold wench she got thick in the waist.

When forty long weeks were over and past
This little bold wench had a big bonny lass.

He also sang a seventh verse not included here:

Oh now that I've got a brave bonny child I'll put it to nurse
Good Lord, it will sink the poor shoemaker's purse.

The final line of the refrain has been borrowed from elsewhere; probably from 'Balaam and Egg', another 'Trooper's Horse' variant.

Although the basic plot is common enough, this particular song is rare and shows signs of considerable age. We know of no broadside or other print sources, and only two oral versions beside Mr Bowditch's seem to survive (a few others currently listed in Roud appear really to be 'Trooper's Horse' fragments): Colm O Lochlainn, *More Irish Street Ballads* (Dublin: Three Candles, 1965), 148–9, 'A Kiss in the Morning Early' and Kinloch, 55–7, 'The Shoemaker'.

THE SOLDIER'S PRAYER

Roud 350

Tune noted by Hume. Ionian, inflexion of 4th.

Quite widespread in English and Scottish tradition, and also found occasionally in Ireland. A broadside was printed by Such, *c*.1870 (see Bodleian, Firth c.14(226) for a copy without imprint) but that is the only one we know of. The song may be older than that; Sharp noted a set from William Stokes at Chew Stoke, Somerset, in 1909 and was apparently told that the song had been learned 'from a singer who was born in 1776'. It seems to have been based on an earlier broadside ballad, 'The Silly Mare and Foal' (Roud 1477) probably printed in York *c*.1810 (British Library, York Publications BL1870c2, No 248) which has also been found in oral tradition on a couple of occasions. This earlier song is a dialogue between a mare and a foal praying for various influential but mistrusted trades (millers, bakers, tailors, publicans and butchers) in the hope that they will get their just desserts.

It has been popular in the armed forces, and has turned up almost everywhere English is spoken. The Such broadside only has about half its content in common with twentieth-century forces versions; the catalogue format easily lends itself to the addition of new stanzas. Bawdy forms are also found in the rugby song repertoire. Dr Graham's text differed a little from the form printed here; Hume quoted verse 1 line 4 as beginning 'And every every thing that you do pray for', which doesn't fit his notation; and in verse 3 the soldier prayed for 'strong' rather than 'good' baccy.

Dr Graham's tune is related to Mr Stokes' and to other oral versions of the period. Lucy Broadwood (*FSJ* V (18) 1914, 72–5) points out a further relationship to an example noted in Ireland, (Petrie, number 771), 'As a Soldier and a Sailor', and, at a greater distance, to the tune 'I'll Tell You a Story' in the ballad opera *The Jovial Crew* (1731). The tune family, in widely varying forms and modes, was much used by English singers; it also includes 'Green Bushes', *q.v.*, 'Sheepcrook and Black Dog' (Roud 948), and the 'Nightingales Sing' tune in this book. More recent versions tend to be sung to forms of 'Villikins and His Dinah'. Recordings from tradition can be heard on Musical Traditions MTCD317–8, *Chainmaker* (George Dunn, Warwickshire: 'Lawyer and Parson'); Veteran VTC5CD, *When the Wind Blows* (Walter Pardon, Norfolk: 'Topman and Afterguard'); and Rounder ROUN1839, *What Will Become of England* (Harry Cox, Norfolk: 'Soldier and Sailor's Prayer').

THE SOLDIER AND HIS TRUE LOVE

Roud 660 Laws O30

Pitts printed at least two versions of this popular song, the first as 'The Sailor and His Truelove' (four stanzas) at his '14 Gt St Andrew St' address before 1819, and then as 'Jemmy's Farewell' (five stanzas) at 6 Gt St Andrew St. Other London printers issued the four-stanza version, while Collard of Bristol issued the five stanza form. It was later published by Such under the title 'The Blackbird and the Thrush', and also by Lancashire and Derby printers. See, among others, Bodleian, Harding B 17(266b) (slips by Jennings and Pigott: 'The Sailor and His Truelove') and Harding B 25(962) (Pitts: 'Jemmy's Farewell'); Harding B 11(301) (Such: 'The Blackbird and Thrush'); Firth c.26(295) (Bebbington of Manchester: 'Blackbird & Thrush'); and Harding B 11(2059) (Plant of Nottingham: 'The Blackbird and Thursh' [sic]).

 Oral versions were typically found in or near sea ports from Gloucester round to the south coast and then up to Norfolk. The Aberdeen area also had plenty of examples (see *Grieg-Duncan* I, 143–9), but in Yorkshire it is only found inland, west of Sheffield, as 'The Castle Hill Anthem'. There are also a few Canadian versions.

 Our text here is from Mrs Bartlett (verses 1 and 4) and Mrs Courtenay (verses 2 and 5); in both cases edited. Verse 3 is probably adapted from one of the broadsides. Mrs Bartlett sang our second verse as follows:

> Says the soldier to his true-love now I must away
> Says the soldier to his true-love I am bound far away
> I am bound to the Indies where the loud cannons roar
> And if ever I return again I will go an see my Nancy
> > *I will go an see my Nancy* (x3)
> > *She's the girl I adore.*

Mrs Courtenay sang our fifth verse (a combination of her third and second), thus:

> Fare thee well, dearest Nancy, I must bid thee adieu
> The big ship is sailing for to collect up her crew.
> The big ship lies floating on a cold flowing tide
> Fare thee well, dearest Nancy, I will make thee my bride.

 Purslow simplified the eighth bar of Mrs Bartlett's tune (the usual one to which this song is sung); we have added Henry Hammond's original notation for that bar, together with a further variant he also noted. Recordings from tradition can be heard on Veteran VTC9CD, *Uncle Tom Cobleigh and All* (Tommy Morrissey and Charlie Pitman, Cornwall: 'Pleasant and Delightful') and VT140CD, *Good Order!* (Edgar Button, Suffolk: 'Pleasant and Delightful'); Rounder CD1839, *What Will Become of England* (Harry Cox, Norfolk: 'Charming and Delightful'); Musical Traditions MTCD304, *Come Hand to Me the Glass* (George Townsend, Sussex: 'The Larks They Sang Melodious'); MT CD 303, *Plenty of Thyme* and Topic TSCD652, *My Ship Shall Sail the Ocean* (Cyril Poacher, Suffolk: 'A Sailor and His True Love').

AN S-O-N-G

Roud 965

Tune noted by Guyer.

A gentle folk song parody which was introduced, as 'Timothy', by Mrs Dorothy Jordan on the stage in 1786, in the musical entertainment *The Virgin Unmasked*, an adaptation from an early work by Henry Fielding. Alfred Moffat and Frank Kidson printed it in their *English Songs of the Georgian Period* (London and Glasgow: Bayley and Ferguson, *c*.1911) and the tune given there is recognisably ancestral to Alfred Stride's. Gardiner (or possibly Guyer) remarked that our tune resembled 'Green Bushes' (Roud 1040, Laws P2) which of course begins with the same line, and referred to a very similar example in *FSJ*, vol I (5) 1904, 243; there is only one verse, but it is almost identical to Mrs Jordan's opening lines. Mr Stride's version has also acquired a reference to 'Oh No, My Love, Not I' (Roud 1403).

There is a broadside issue without imprint in the Madden Collection (Slip Songs H–N, Reel 72, item 1267, Vaughan Williams Memorial Library) and Baring-Gould included a further text, in terms of content somewhere between Jordan and Stride, in his *Book of Nursery Songs and Rhymes* (1895; number XIV, 'Among the Green Hay'), noting: 'This is an old nursery song that I have had from an old lady in Devon, who heard it from her grandmother. She forgot two of the verses, but Miss L E Broadwood has kindly supplied me with them from a Hampshire singer.' This may perhaps be the *FSJ* example, which came from 'an old lady born in 1800 or 1801 ... a native of Hampshire'.

There is also a vague resemblance in the melody to the ubiquitous 'Villikins and his Dinah', and the only other version of this song that we know of, which was collected from Mrs Freda Palmer in Oxfordshire in 1969 and published in *FMJ* I (4) 1969, 330–331, was sung to that melody. Mrs Palmer's set can be heard on *Up in the North, Down in the South: Songs and Tunes from the Mike Yates Collection 1964–2000* (Musical Traditions MTCD311–2, 2001).

SOUR GRAPES

Roud 3713

Tune noted by Guyer. Ionian, no 7th. F♯ removed from key signature as that note does not occur in the tune.

This song, based on Æsop's well known fable, was written by Thomas Dibdin (son of the enormously prolific songwriter Charles Dibdin) and first appeared in his musical entertainment *The Naval Pillar, or, Britannia's Triumph*, first produced at the Theatre Royal, Covent Garden, in October 1799, where it was sung by Joseph Shepherd Munden. It was published in songsters and on broadsides; see Bodleian, Harding B 22(92): a slip printed by M Bowley, No 96, Aldersgate Street, London, *c.*1799. There was also a parody, 'The blue tail'd fly', for which, see Firth b.26(36) and other editions.

The song evidently remained popular, and was included in *The Universal Songster* vol III (1826) 88, and – with music – in *120 Comic Songs Sung by Sam Cowell, c.*1860. Frank Gamblin appears to have forgotten part of the first verse, and lines 2–5 here have been added from a print source. No other version seems to have been found in Britain, but it has turned up occasionally in the USA and Canada. The tune is described as 'Welsh' in *120 Comic Songs*; it is almost identical to Gamblin's, and is even in the same key. That being so, it seems likely that the lines Gamblin forgot were from Cowell's version:

> And as they hung they seemed to say
> To him who underneath did stay
> If you can fetch me down you may.

THE SPRIG OF THYME

Roud 3

Tune noted by Guyer.

Although the original of this seventeenth-century ballad appears not to have survived, it is unquestionably answered on a broadside of 1696, printed by Alexander Milbourne (Pepys 5.246) titled 'An Excellent new Song Called, The Young-Man's Answer to the Maids Garden of Tyme, To a pleasant New Tune'. Stanza 3 puts the connection beyond doubt:

> You say a young man went into your garden fine
> And there unto your discontent he pluckt up all your time.

The responses make it quite clear that the metaphors are mostly sexual in nature. Pepys 5.246 can be seen at the website of the University of Santa Barbara: http://emc.english.ucsb.edu/ballad_project/

Chappell (II, 521), quoting from Whittaker's *History of the Parish of Whalley* (1801) 318, states that the original was supposedly written by Mrs Fleetwood Habergham of Habergham Hall, Lancashire, *c.*1690. Although anecdotal attributions of this sort cannot always be trusted, the dates certainly fit. The song persisted in oral tradition and was introduced by the popular actress Mrs Honey to the London stage in James Robinson Planché's one-act Vaudeville *The Loan of a Lover* at the Olympic Theatre, 1834.

It appears in many English and Scottish song collections of the eighteenth and nineteenth centuries and was reprinted in street literature under a wide variety of titles. Forrest of Edinburgh, for instance, issued it as 'The Maid's Lament for the loss of her Maiden-head' in 1766 (BL 11621. b. 6 [13], reproduced in Reeves, *Everlasting Circle*, 237). Pitts, Catnach and their followers, plus the usual midlands and northern printers, put out their own editions, and it was printed in Ireland by Kelly of Waterford. See, for example, Bodleian, Harding B 11(2793): 'Sprig of Thyme', printed by J O Bebbington of Manchester between 1855 and 1858.

We have no version of the closely related 'The Seeds of Love', which shares a number of stanzas, earlier than Pitts' edition (see Bodleian, Harding B 11(1657)). It shows every sign of having been a rewrite intended to capitalise on the popularity of 'Sprig of Thyme', and if so, it achieved that aim with some distinction; Chappell (II, 735) described it, along with 'Cupid's Garden' and 'Early One Morning', as one of the three 'most popular songs among the servant-maids of the present generation' (late 1850s). Another spin-off was 'The Posy of Thyme' issued by Collard of Bristol (for another edition, 'The Poesy of Thyme', see Holloway and Black, I, 215). Needless to say, both 'Sprig of Thyme' and 'Seeds of Love' have been enormously popular, and found in tradition almost everywhere where English is spoken.

Our verses 1, 4 and 6 are from David Marlow; the rest, and the tune, is from Moses Blake. Traditional examples of 'Sprig of Thyme' can be heard on EFDSS CD002, *A Century of Song* (Billy Bartle, 'Come All You Garners Gay'); Topic TSCD662, *We've Received Orders to Sail* and Musical Traditions MTCD303, *Plenty of Thyme* (Cyril Poacher, 'Plenty of Thyme'); and Veteran VT129CD, *I've Come to Sing a Song* (Vic Legg, 'Garners Gay').

SWANSEA TOWN

Roud 929

Tune noted by Balfour Gardiner.

Previously classed with Roud 165, 'Adieu Sweet Lovely Nancy', a broadside song from which it is obviously derived, though there seem to be no broadside examples of 'Swansea Town' itself. In its current form it was crystallised – presumably – in Swansea and from there taken the short journey by sea to Cork, where it became very popular as 'The Holy Ground'. This Hampshire version from William Randall – a naval pensioner, aged 55 when Gardiner met him – is a perfect example of an interim version between what have become two distinct and separate songs. Stan Hugill, *Shanties from the Seven Seas* (London: Routledge & Kegan Paul, 1961), prints three examples: 180, 'Old Swansea Town Once More' and 181, 'The Holy Ground Once More' are forms of the our song, with related tunes; while 179, 'Old Swansea Town Once More', is a shanty proper, sharing title and chorus only. Kenneth Peacock, *Songs Of The Newfoundland Outports* (Ottawa: National Museum of Canada, 1965), vol 3, 877, prints a version, 'Good-bye My Lovely Annie' which, though it lacks a chorus, is otherwise very close to ours, with a related tune and the repeated couplet:

> But still I live in hopes to see you
> In Newfoundland once more.

Mr Randall sang 'still I live', not 'still I lives' as printed in the original edition. For broadside copies of the earlier song, see Bodleian, Harding B 11(2667): 'New Sailor's Farewell' (J Pitts); Firth c.12(171): 'My Lovely Nancy' (J Walker of Durham); Harding B 11(3899): 'Adieu My Lovely Nancy' (J Catnach); and others.

THE TAILOR AND THE CROW

Roud 891

Dixon-Bell, (Ballad LIX) presents an ingenious thesis arguing that the carrion crow is Charles II, and all of the song's contents are accounted for in terms of religious and political references; though he was unable to identify the 'Taylor'. *ODNR* number 87, however, quotes a few lines from a commonplace book of Charles I's time (Sloane MS 1489 fol 17, c.1627); these are equivalent to our verses 3 and 5.

In eight stanzas, the song appeared on several issues by Pitts of London (see Bodleian, Harding B 12(10) and 2806 c.18(55), for example) and in the late eighteenth century was quoted in various items of literature. Deeming of Boston, Massachusetts, printed a version called 'The Sly Young Crow'; this can be seen at the Library of Congress website, *America Singing* (http://memory.loc.gov/ammem/amsshtml/). It was, and still is, popular in the southern half of England and is widespread in the USA and Canada in a variety of forms; Helen Creighton, for instance, found it in Nova Scotia as 'A Kangaroo Sat on an Oak'.

Our verses 3 and 5 are not from William Bartlett, but are added from other versions; 5 seems to be adapted from a text printed by Williams, 227. The text here has been polished up in places; Mr Bartlett began: 'Now as I walked out one May morning ... When the birds began to whistle, Ha! then I began to sing'. In verse 2, he sang (notebook transcription):

Now that false carrion crow O! he stood upon a bough
And he swore he saw the tailor cutting cabbage out of straw

In the folder transcription, the first line reads: 'Now that false carrion crow then he stands upon his hose'. In verse 7, line 2, Mr Bartlett sang: 'He's got the blackpot and pig's guts in his house'. Gardiner got a version from Henry Stansbridge (H417; see *Everlasting Circle*, 256), and his equivalent verse, which ran on more usual lines, may have been used to amend Bartlett's:

Never mind, said the tailor, I don't care a louse
For we shall have black puddings, chitterlings and souse.

No music is given for part of the chorus: 'In singing "Pork ba-a-con (be-a-con), Pork Be-a-con"', remarked Hammond, 'Bartlett imitated a crow capitally but I cannot put what he sang into musical form.'

More recently, the song was in the repertoire of the late Walter Pardon, but no recording is available commercially.

THE TAILOR'S BREECHES

Roud 1610

The *Marrow Bones* text is a composite of Robert Barratt's two stanzas and Jacob Baker's five. In the latter's version the inn is called 'The Roving Nightingale'. Tailors in folk song are frequently the victims of humiliation, while sailors regularly lose their money, and sometimes their trousers, to ladies of easy virtue. The only other two south coast versions, (one and four stanzas) were collected by Gardiner in Hampshire (H82 and H539) and are titled 'The Sailor's Trousers'; the action takes place in Covent Garden.

There is one further example known; Arthur Wood's magnificent version from the Whitby area (see Hudleston, *Songs of the Ridings*, Scarborough: G A Pinder and Son, 2001, 261) has eleven stanzas and has obviously been expanded and reworked by a true comic (perhaps Wood himself); it is very much localised to Whitby. For only five versions to have survived – and those quite different – is remarkable, especially with no obvious print source; we know of no surviving broadside examples, though a broadside origin does seem likely. Thomas Hardy (a near contemporary of Barratt, whose Piddletown, already at that time well into its transformation into the more genteel Puddletown, was Hardy's fictional Weatherbury) refers to 'The Tailor's Breeches' twice in *Tess of the d'Urbervilles* (chapters 40 and 49) and once in *A Few Crusted Characters*, chapter 2, 'Tony Kytes, the Arch-deceiver': 'He used to sing "The Tailor's Breeches" with a religious manner, as if it were a hymn:–

O the petticoats went off, and the breeches they went on!

and all the rest of the scandalous stuff.'

THORNABY WOODS

Roud 222

Ionian with inflexion of 7th.

Like other local poaching songs, this one from Nottinghamshire has been spread around England, largely by broadside printers. There are copies from Pitts (Bodleian, Harding B 11(2692 and other impressions), Catnach (Harding B 17(311b)) and other London printers, right up to Walker and Hoggett of Durham (Harding B 25(1898)), but we don't know of one from Nottinghamshire, nor of a traditional example from that county, though oral versions have been found in sixteen different English counties and in Ohio, USA. There are, however, broadside copies from Ford of Chesterfield and (probably) Crome of Sheffield (Harding B 28(237)); neither city is very far from Newark.

Dixon-Bell, Ballad LXVII, note: 'The song finds locality in the village of Thornehagh, in the hundred of Newark. The common, or Moor-fields, was inclosed about 1797, and is now no longer called by the ancient designation. It contains eight hundred acres. The manor of Thornehagh is the property of the ancient family of Nevile, who have a residence on the estate.' Thorney Wood Chase, part of Sherwood Forest near Newark-on-Trent, enclosed about 1790, has also been suggested by Peter Kennedy; but this seems less likely. Roy Palmer, *Everyman's Book of English Country Songs*, London: J M Dent, 1979, 96, points out that it was too much deforested to have offered much scope for poaching.

Mrs Webb's tune is similar to that of another poaching song, 'The Death of Poor Bill Brown' (Roud 609), made on an event of 1769 at Brightside, Sheffield. She had only a fragment of text; our verse 1 and verses 2, line 1, and 3, line 3. The rest of the text appears to have been adapted from Gardiner H938 (from an unnamed source, probably at Axford) and from the version sung by Harry Cox of Norfolk, which is printed in Kennedy, *Folksongs of Britain and Ireland*, 570–1.

Versions from traditional singers can be heard on Musical Traditions MTCD317–8, *Chainmaker* (George Dunn, Warwickshire); MTCD 320, *Here's Luck to a Man* (Jasper Smith, Surrey) and MTCD305–6, *Put a Bit of Powder on it Father* (Walter Pardon, Norfolk); and on Veteran VT119CD, *Catch Me if you Can: Songs from Cornish Travellers* (Sophie Legg, Cornwall) and VT129CD, *I've Come to Sing a Song* (Vic Legg, Cornwall); and Topic TSCD668, *To Catch a Fine Buck was My Delight* (Jasper Smith again).

THE THREE BUTCHERS

Roud 17 Laws L4

Mixolydian.

At least three seventeenth-century copies of 'The Three Worthy Butchers of the North', written by Paul Burges, have survived. One, printed by P Brooksby in West-Smithfield, is dated *c.*1672–9 (see *Roxburghe* VII, 59). Here the three butchers are named Kitson, Wilson and Johnson, the last of these having done well to survive for three centuries, albeit with the aid of print in one form or another. Perhaps this is because he is the hero who stays to fight while the other two cowards flee. This version has 102 lines and a chorus. Dated slightly later, at 1685–97, is 'A New Ballad of the Three Merry Butchers' (*Roxburghe* VII, 62), which has eleven double stanzas. Copies of this version survive in almost all of the main seventeenth-century ballad collections. For examples, see Bodleian, Douce Ballads 3(92b) (Newcastle); Douce Ballads 3(91b) (Aldermary Church-Yard, Bow-lane); and Pepys 2.176 (J Bissell at the Bible and Harp, West-Smithfield).

It continued to be reprinted in this form during the eighteenth century and into the nineteenth, when a ten-stanza version was printed in Ireland. During the early C19 it was reduced to nine stanzas and then eight. In this final form it was reprinted all over England, but by then the two cowards' names had been reduced to 'Ips and Gips'. Various copies can be seen at the Bodleian site as 'Three Butchers', 'Ips, Gips, and Johnson; or the Three Butchers' and 'A New Song on / call'd The Three Huntsmen's Tragedy' (a re-written form printed by Haly of Cork and Brereton of Dublin).

As might be expected, it is widespread and popular throughout the English-speaking world. Our text is amended in places from other versions in the Hammond and Gardiner MSS and from broadsides. In place of our verses 7–9, Mr Stockley sang:

> Then he took her up all on his horse and they rode along so far
> They rode till they came to a lonesome lane and there began to talk
> When she poked her fingers in her ears and loudly screamed and cried
> Out sprang ten bold high robber men with weapons in their hand.

He sang our verse 12 thus:

> But this wicked woman who was standing by, she thought it very cruel
> She drew a pistol from her side and shot him through and through.

In the final line, Johnson was the *handsomest* butcher; 'finest' is more usual, however. Mr Stockley lacked our verse 13, which is probably borrowed (and slightly rewritten) from the standard broadside text. Forms of his tune are often used with this song, though there are others as well. Examples from tradition can be heard on Topic TSCD514, *A World Without Horses* (Walter Pardon, Norfolk) and TSCD512D, *The Bonny Labouring Boy* (Harry Cox, Norfolk); and on Musical Traditions MTCD307, *Band of Gold* (Biggun Smith, Gloucestershire).

THREE JOLLY HUNTSMEN

Roud 796

Tune noted by Guyer: here transposed up a fifth.

An enquiry in *Notes and Queries* (3rd series, VI, Nov 19 1864, 415) quoting a single verse and chorus, elicited a reply to the effect that the full words were to be found in *Songs of the Chace* (2nd edition, London: Sherwood, Neely & Jones, 1811). The song is rather older than that; Baring-Gould (*A Book of Nursery Songs and Rhymes*, London: 1895, 11) quotes a text titled 'The Three Jovial Welshmen'. It is close to ours, though longer and with two additional verses of Baring-Gould's own making. He noted: 'In a collection of "Forty Early Ballad Books" in the British Museum, No. 21 is ["The Woody Choristers"], and this contains the "Three Jovial Welshmen".' *ODNR* number 525, 'There Were Three Jovial Welshmen' (Roud 283) dates *The Woody Choristers* to *c*.1770 and adds that our song appeared there as 'The Pursuit of Reynard'. Also quoted is the following, from unspecified 'sheet music about 1725', with the comment that it may have been old even then:

> There was 3 Jovial Welshmen, & they w^d. hunt ye Fox;
> And where sh^d. they find bold Reynolds, but among ye Woods & Rocks.
> W^th a gibble, gibble, gibble, all in a merry tone,
> W^th a hoop, hoop, hoop & hallow, & so cry'd 'ery one.

The song has been fairly widespread in England, though we have only a few oral versions; Roud also lists one Scottish and one Irish example. It is rather better known in the USA. The chorus varies considerably, but usually attempts to replicate some of the sounds of the hunt. Roud 283 is more common in tradition, and forms of it survive from the early seventeenth century. There may be some relationship between the two song groups; both concern a hunting expedition undertaken by three men, but ours is relatively straightforward while the other becomes progressively more and more surreal.

William Taylor repeated each verse couplet twice. His chorus has been amended to restore the rhyme scheme, and his third verse ended 'He swore he saw bold Reynard [sic] run in the hollow glen'. Verse 4 is introduced from elsewhere; perhaps adapted from the text in Williams, 67–8. There seem to be no recordings available from English tradition, but an American example can be heard at the website of the Max Hunter Folk Song Collection (http://maxhunter.missouristate.edu/) as 'A Fox Huntin'', sung by Fred High, Arizona, 1959.

TOO MANY LOVERS

Roud 1611

This song on a popular theme appeared as 'Young Susan had Lovers' in Richard Brinsley Peake's one-act farce or comic operetta *The Middle Temple or, Which Is My Son?* produced at the Theatre Royal in 1829. The music was by George Herbert Rodwell, who wrote all the music for the play, while the text was by John Baldwin Buckstone, the comedian, playwright and theatre manager who wrote the play 'Green Bushes' among a good many others. It was sung by the popular actress Mrs Mary Anne Keeley in the character of 'Penelope, a maid', who introduced it thus:

'I wish that footman would give me an opportunity of saying summit civil to him – la! but I could do it. I would not stand shilly-shally as my friend Susan did, and lose all her sweethearts.'

The song was published by Goulding & D'Almaine and the lyric – without tune – appeared in songsters and on broadsides until quite late in the nineteenth century; see, for example, Bodleian: Harding B 11(2106), printed by Pitts of Seven Dials. Other editions were published by Catnach and Birt in London, Livesy of Manchester, Harkness of Preston, and Marr of Glasgow. Captain Marryat quoted the text in chapter 13 of his novel *Jacob Faithful* (1834). Mrs Young's version appears to be the only example noted by folk song collectors; she knew it by its original title, 'Young Susan had Lovers' ('Too Many Lovers' is editorial) and her text – tidied up a little here – was not greatly changed from printed forms. She pronounced 'lovers' in the old way: 'lovyers'.

The text of Peake's play, as published in 1840 by Webster and Co., can be seen at the University of Indiana's Library Electronic Text Resource Service (LETRS) public facility: http://www.letrs.indiana.edu/cgi-bin/eprosed/eprosed-idx?coll=eprosed;idno=P3.0507

THE TREADMILL SONG

Roud 1077

Tune: Dorian, no 6th or 7th.

The widely printed broadside 'County Gaol' gave rise to a whole series of localisations (the title was sometimes given as '— Gaol' for that very purpose) such as 'Bellevue Gaol', 'Wakefield Gaol', 'Preston Gaol', 'Kirkdale Gaol', and so on; copies of these and others can be seen at the Bodleian Library Broadside Ballads website. They seem to have had some currency inside prisons as well as out. Although distinct from our song, the pattern is similar and there are textual overlaps; Steve Gardham recently collected a Hull localisation, 'Hedon

Road Gaol', which shares our stanza 5. 'The Owslebury Lads' (Roud 17212), noted by Hammond (H333) and Gardiner (H204) from James Stagg, Winchester, 1906, is also made on much the same pattern.

The text printed here is a collation from three sources. Verse 1 and verse 2, lines 3 and 4, are from the related song 'Taunton Gaol' (Roud 3469), noted by Cecil Sharp from Tom Spracklan (Somerset) in 1903 (Sharp MSS, *Folk Words* 39–40 / *Folk Tunes* 23; see also Richards & Stubbs, *The English Folksinger*, Glasgow & London: Collins, 1979, 207–208). Verse 2, lines 1 and 2, and verses 5, 7 and 8 are from William Davey, while verses 3, 4, 6 and 9 are from Sam Gregory. Mr Gregory had a further verse, which would fit after our stanza 8:

> At 12 o'clock our beef comes in
> Sometimes fat and sometimes lean
> But devil of a word we must not say
> To bread and water all next day.

Mr Davey's final two verses were:

> Now Saturday is come I'm sorry to say
> Sunday is our starvation day
> Our jackboots and our goglets too
> They are not ready nor they will not do.

> Now six long months is gone and past
> I'll return to my bonny lass
> We'll leave the turnkeys all behind
> The wheel to tread and the corn to grind.

A goglet was a water container, typically earthenware. 'Skilly' (verse 5) was a thin gruel. 'Dukis' (verse 9) is written 'Dukès' in the MS. Mr Gregory's chorus was of the 'fal the diddle' type; in the original edition of *Marrow Bones*, the opening 'To my' in the final line of Mr Davey's chorus was omitted, making a very effective pause; here, we have restored it as an alternative.

Davey's and Gregory's versions, and combinations of them, have often been anthologised, usually under their MS title, 'Gaol Song'. See *CEFS* 22 for one such, and *FSJ* VII (27) 1923, 47–8, for both texts with their tunes. Mr Gregory's melody was very different. Henry Hammond wrote, 'Davy's gaol-bird is miserable and sings to an appropriately weird tune, whilst Gregory's is a humorous fellow, who sings in the major key.' Mr Davey's melody is pentachordal, on five consecutive notes of the scale; Vaughan Williams thought it Aeolian, while Lucy Broadwood inclined to the Dorian mode. It has rather the flavour of certain lullabies and luck-visiting songs such as the version of the 'Souling Song' (Roud 304) printed in Broadwood 30–31. A L Lloyd discusses the subject in *Folk Song in England*, chapter 1, 'The Foundations of Folk Song'.

THE TROOPER'S HORSE

Roud 1613

Tune noted by Gamblin.

This song first appears in *Pills* (V, 13–14) as 'The Trooper Watering his Nagg'. It was issued on broadsides, but only one late eighteenth-century example, without imprint, has survived: 'A New Song Called Ball my Nagg' in the Madden Collection (Slip Songs H–N [VWML microfilm 72] item 1320). It has the four-line stanzas of the *Pills* version, but is closer textually to our Hampshire set. Instead of a trooper we have a 'jolly dragoon'; the daughter is Nan on the broadside and Siss in *Pills*.

Mrs Goodyear did not sing this song in a very regular form. She wrote down the words for Gardiner as follows:

Verse 1. First couplet; second couplet; third couplet (first line); refrain (first line); third couplet (second line); refrain (second line).

Verse 2. Fourth couplet (first line); refrain (first line); fourth couplet (second line); refrain (second line).

Verse 3. Fifth couplet (first line); refrain (first line); fourth couplet (second line); refrain (second line); sixth couplet; refrain (second line).

Gamblin's MS notation reflects the arrangement of her first composite verse. Purslow has opted here for the second format, and has rearranged the text and music accordingly; the tune shown is, therefore, Gamblin's bars 1 and 2; 3 and 11 conflated; 12 to 17. There are traces of the tune published by D'Urfey in Mrs Goodyear's, though it is much changed. Verses 5 and 6 in our text here are not from Mrs Goodyear, but are adapted from D'Urfey:

Quoth she what is this so stiff and warm...
'Tis Ball my Nag he will do you no harm...

Quoth he what is this? Quoth she 'tis a Well...
Where Ball your Nag may drink his fill...

Unsurprisingly, collectors have found few examples in tradition. Cecil Sharp got a version from James Bishop at Priddy, Somerset, in 1905. 'Ball my Nag' had become 'Balaam and Egg,' so what remained of the narrative was a little confusing. Karpeles (II, 380 and 628) simply treated it as 'a nonsense song', while remarking that 'the first stanza, minus the refrain, is to be found in Opie [*ODNR*] No. 542.' Mr Bishop's interleaved refrain was very close to that of 'Green as the Leaves are Green', a one-verse fragment noted by the Hammonds from William Bartlett (D625). Mr Bartlett's verse almost certainly belonged to this song rather than to 'The Shoemaker's Kiss', *q.v.*, with which it has been combined in *Marrow Bones*.

A L Lloyd noted a remarkably complete set – with a tune related to Mrs Goodyear's – near Leiston, Suffolk, in 1941 (*Folk Song in England*, 204–6), adding that essentially the same story had been found in Russian folk tales. As recently as 1988, Gwilym Davies recorded a version, 'Green Lived Upon the Green,' from Bob Cross, a retired businessman of Witcombe, Gloucestershire. A sound recording in the Edith Fowke Collection at York University, Toronto, Ontario, 'The Grass that Grows on the Brim' (Owen McBride, 1994) may also be a version of this song, though at present Roud classes it on its own at number 4840.

THE TURTLE DOVE

Roud 422

Aeolian.

Another lament that has passed to and fro between oral tradition, the stall presses and art song since at least the 1680s. Two broadsides of that period are likely sources of the later, shorter cheap print forms. Probably the earlier of the two is 'The Two Constant Lovers; or the Prentice Obtain'd his Master's Daughter by True Love and Loyalty' (Pepys 5.322) printed by J Blare, 1684–1702. This contains seven of the general stock of stanzas, appearing in a block as verses 10–16 of a total of twenty-one. The other, 'The Unkind Parents; or The Languishing Lamentation of the Two Loyal Lovers' printed by C Bates 1885–9 (See *Roxburghe* VII 552) also has seven of the general stock, but in the same order as the later printed version (stanzas 1, 2, 4, 5, 7, 13, 14 and 16 of a total of sixteen, one being split amongst two non-stock stanzas). These texts, and others, are quoted in Steve Gardham's article 'The Turtle Dove' at *Musical Traditions*: http://www.mustrad.org.uk/articles/dung20.htm

During the eighteenth century the ballad became so popular as to influence new compositions like Burns' 'Red, Red, Rose' and Barham's 'There Sits a Bird on Yonder

Tree' (*Ingoldsby Legends*, 3rd Series). Various writers on Burns mention a garland of 1770, 'The Horn Fair Garland' containing 'The Turtle Dove, or True Love's Farewell'. Burns is supposed to have owned a copy.

Round about 1800 the ballad was printed under the title 'The True Lover's Farewel' on at least three separate slips, none with any imprint (see Bodleian, Firth c.18(101)). This is the most influential seven-stanza version, but there are plenty of oral examples, particularly in Scotland, that contain verses from earlier versions. In 1856 it was burlesqued for the American music hall as 'My Mary Ann' by Barney Williams; this also became popular in oral tradition on both sides of the Atlantic, having been published in England on sheet music in the same year. Williams and his wife also performed successfully in London around this time. See Bodleian, Johnson Ballads 1111 and other copies; and the Lester Levy Collection for sheet music.

Edith Sartin's text was fragmentary; ours is a collation, further amended in places. Verse 2, lines 1 and 2 are from Mrs Sartin; 3 and 4 are from Mr Bridle. Verses 2 and 3: Mr Bridle. Verses 4 to 6: Mrs Russell. Verse 1 is introduced from an unidentified source; perhaps modified from 'The True Lover's Farewell', though similar forms occur in many oral versions.

The lament is found all over the English-speaking world under numerous titles and in a wide range of forms, but has been particularly popular in southern England, Scotland, the southern USA and the Appalachians. A recording from English tradition can be heard at the *Collect Britain* website: EFDSS Cylinder No.50. (David Penfold, Sussex, 1907: 'Turtle Dove') – it isn't in very good shape, but the tune is recognisably a variant of Mrs Sartin's. An American example is on Musical Traditions MTCD322, *Far in the Mountains 2* and EFDSS CD002, *A Century of Song* (Evelyn Ramsey, North Carolina: 'Truelover's Farewell'). See also the Max Hunter Collection website ('The Blackest Crow' and other titles).

THE UNFORTUNATE TAILOR

Roud 1614

Tune noted by Gamblin, later amended by Vaughan Williams. Aeolian, no 6th. The variation in bar 3 was ambiguous in the original edition, so here it is shown separately.

'I'll Go and Enlist for a Sailor: a quaint pathetic serio-comic ballad' ('Song of the Unfortunate Tailor') is from the repertoire of the enormously popular musical entertainer Harry Clifton (1831–1872), and was probably written by him, *c.* 1865. A number of Clifton's songs have turned up in oral tradition; 'On Board of the *Kangaroo*', 'Dark Girl Dress'd in Blue' and 'My Rattling Mare and I', among others. He was also responsible for 'Rocky Road to Dublin' and 'Lannigan's Ball', though these were written for him by D K Gavan ('The Galway Poet').

Mr Lovett's melody is a form of the Irish 'Shule Agra' or 'Shule Aroon', well known in the English countryside at that time. Cecil Sharp found another form, rather different, used in Sherborne for the morris dance 'Go and List for a Sailor'; Mr Oliver's tune, by contrast, seems completely unrelated. Apart from these and an example in Alfred Williams' MS collection, the song has not been recorded by collectors. It appeared on broadsides; see, for example, Bodleian, Firth c.12(384): Poet's Box, Glasgow, 1868.

We have described in the Introduction how the text printed in the original edition of *Marrow Bones* came to be garbled. Here, it is restored to its correct order. Verses 1, 2, 3, 5, 6, 7 and 9 are from George Lovett, with some small modifications from Alfred Oliver, whose version provides our verses 4 and 8. In verse 7, 'When telling my love' was printed as '*Without guessing* my love'; this was an attempt to make sense of 'Without telling my love', a copyist's error which we have corrected here from Gardiner's notebook (number 8, page 107). The preceding lines, which Mr Lovett had forgotten, explain all; we quote them here from the broadside cited:

I went to plead but she did refuse
She loved another, so I must excuse
Her candour, but it was no use
She never could marry a tailor!
When telling my love, in came that Cobb (*etc.*)

In verse 4, Mr Oliver's 'looked crow' may perhaps be an expression on the lines of the nautical 'look Cro'-Jack-eyed' (to squint: see Partridge, *Dictionary of Slang and Unconventional English*) but the broadside simply has 'looked cross'. A wax cylinder recording that is probably George Lovett singing 'Farewell Lovely Nancy' (Roud 527 Laws K14) can be heard at the British Library's *Collect Britain* website (http://www.collectbritain.co.uk/): EFDSS Cylinder No.23.

THE UNQUIET GRAVE

Roud 51 Child 78

Aeolian.

Three different versions were printed on broadsides. The earliest, without imprint, is 'The Mournful Lovers' of *c*.1800 (Madden Collection), with nine stanzas; this appears to have been taken from existing oral tradition, and the stanzas are somewhat out of order. It doesn't appear to have had direct influence on surviving oral versions. A second, 'The Weeping Lover', has nine stanzas and was printed in slightly variant forms by both Wright and Heppel in Birmingham (see Bodleian, 2806 c.17(460) and 2806 c.17(461)), and Williams at Portsea. It shows evidence of having had influence on a few midlands versions. A third, with seven stanzas, was printed by Jackson and Pratt in Birmingham as 'Cold blows the wind' (Harding B 11(634)). Comparing available oral versions closely with these three forms, it would appear that the majority have not been directly influenced by them. It seems likely that there were earlier stall versions which have not survived, but there is no real evidence that the song is particularly old, in despite of the imaginative speculations of some commentators. For detailed analyses of various aspects of the song, see David Atkinson, 'The Wit Combat Episode in "The Unquiet Grave"' in *Lore and Language*, 12, 1994, 11–30; Bronson II, 234–245; Child II, 234–238; and Ruth Harvey, 'The Unquiet Grave' in *JEFDSS* IV (2) 1941, 49–66.

Jane Hann's version (her brother Henry Way also sang it, but the Hammonds didn't note it from him) is one of the most complete ever found, containing material not in any surviving broadsides, though she lacks the 'wit combat' verses that occur in them and in some oral examples. Her text has been amended in places. She sang 'as any young man *or* may' in verse 2: this can be understood either as 'as any young man or maid' or as printed here, assuming 'or' to have been merely a syllabic extension of 'man'. The song is normally recounted from a woman's point of view, but 'man' does occur in a few oral versions. Her eighth verse ran:

Is withered to a stalk, sweetheart
And never more shall be
And I shall be along with thee
A-lying in my grave.

Verses 9 and 10 are unusual. The former occurs elsewhere once only, in Hammond S36, Mrs Gulliver, Combe Florey, Somerset, 1905 and the latter only in Devon examples from Baring-Gould's collections (*Songs of the West*, 1905, 12–13; *Everlasting Circle* 272–3; and Child IV, 474–5). The first two lines of verse 11 were missing and have been added from Hammond's notebook 6, where they appear opposite page 33. Mrs Hann's tune ('the only tune that Dorset singers seem to have to "Unquiet Grave"', noted Hammond) was of two lines only; lines 3 and 4 as printed here. Essentially they are the second half of the well known 'Lazarus' melody; what Frank Purslow seems to have done is reconstruct a classic

'Lazarus' form by using the fourth line (unchanged) for our line 2, and for line 1 with the final note dropped from D to F, as in line 3. He left the verses set out as quatrains, however, and we have retained that arrangement. A recording from tradition can be heard on Musical Traditions MTCD317–8, *Chainmaker* (George Dunn, Warwickshire).

THE UPS AND DOWNS

Roud 364

Tune noted by Guyer.

We first find this song as 'The Maid of Tottenham' in *Choyce Drollery*, 1656, with nine six-line stanzas, triple rhyming and a 'derry down' chorus (see Pinto and Rodway, 329–331). Thomas D' Urfey printed a considerably different version in *Pills*, IV, 179, set to the tune 'London is a Fine Town', as 'Tottingham Frolick'. In the late eighteenth century it appeared in a garland as 'The Darlington Maid going to Market' with only five stanzas, but still a 'derry down' chorus (Robert White Collection, Newcastle University Library, 17.42). In the mid-nineteenth century, Disley of London printed a five-stanza rewrite, 'Dublin Jack, the Rover', which by then had developed the four-line form sung by our Mr Frankham, but the 'fol-le-lol' refrain was still 'derry down' at that point, though the maid was now going to Salisbury instead of London.

Titles vary considerably among oral versions, and the maid's destination varies from Aylesbury through Salisbury, Happisburgh (pronounced Haysboro'), Hazelbury, Hastings, Osbury and Roseberry, to Derby. It has been found mostly in the southern counties (Gardiner and the Hammonds got several examples, and Sharp two) and in East Anglia. It has also been reported in a few widely dispersed versions in North America. It is usually sung to variants of the same tune – a near relative of 'The Lincolnshire Poacher' – that Mr Frankham used. He ended verse 3 'where the grass is growing high' rather than 'all under a shady tree', which has been borrowed from another version.

Reeves (*Idiom of the People*, 123–4) noted: '*The Ups and Downs*: the 69th Foot Regiment, so nicknamed perhaps because 69 reads the same when it is upside down. Until it became the 2nd Battalion of the Welsh Regiment, in about 1881, this was a mixed force of old crocks and young recruits who at one time served as marines.'

Recordings from tradition can be heard on Veteran VT154CD, *Good Hearted Fellows* (Fred Whiting, Suffolk); Musical Traditions MTCD311–2, *Up in the North and Down in the South* (Jack Goodban, Kent) and MTCD400, *Down the Cherry Tree* (George Maynard, Sussex); and Topic TSCD665, *As Me and My Love Sat Courting* (George Maynard).

A WEEK'S WORK WELL DONE

Roud 433 Laws Q6

Tune noted by Gamblin. Ionian, no 7th. C$^\sharp$ removed from key signature, as that note does not occur in the tune.

Baring-Gould (*Songs of the West*) refers to a ballad in 'West Country Garlands' *c.*1760 (BM 1161, b11) of eleven stanzas; he quotes the first four, which tell of the man's happy state prior to marriage, but notes that 'most singers begin with the fifth verse'; by which he presumably means the first in his version, which was noted from Robert Hard, whose text (including the chorus) differs only in minor particulars from Alfred Porter's, and whose tune, though distinct, is clearly related.

A late eighteenth-century version of seven stanzas with the title 'Holly Twig' was printed by Evans of London, Pitts, and Collard of Bristol [Madden Collection]. Croshaw of York printed a slightly later version of six stanzas under the title 'Week's Work Completed' (Bodleian, Harding B 25(2022)) and there were other versions under different titles printed in the early nineteenth century. These later versions start with the 'Monday morning' stanza as in Mr Porter's version. There is also a rewritten version in Healy, *The Mercier Book of Old Irish Street Ballads*, 4, 133, titled 'A New Song Called The Week's Marriage' which lacks the holly twig; instead the wife is dispatched by poisoning her tea with jalop. Variations on the same theme include 'A Week's Matrimony', 'Woeful Marriage' and (with the sexes reversed) 'I Was Married a Week'; examples of these can be seen at the Bodleian website. Of course the 'holly twig' motif and the general subject immediately bring to mind 'The Wife Wrapt in Wether's Skin' (Roud 117, Child 277).

Oral versions are found in southern England and the USA, where it has been particularly popular in Virginia and North Carolina. There appear to be no recordings from British tradition, but American examples can be heard at the websites of the Max Hunter Collection ('Little Willie Green') and the Wolf Folklore Collection ('Willow Green').

WILL THE WEAVER

Roud 432 Laws Q9

Tune noted by Gamblin. Ionian, no 6th.

Widespread throughout the English-speaking world, this song has survived particularly well in the USA, where both Huddie Ledbetter ('Leadbelly') and Doc Watson recorded versions, as 'Billy the Weaver' and 'Everyday Dirt' respectively. Early versions are set out as a dialogue, which might suggest an eighteenth-century theatrical origin. A copy in the National Library of Scotland (L.C.2900(7)) is entitled 'Will the weaver, or The bridegroom's garland : in three parts. Part I. A dialogue between a new married man and his mother, about the wickedness of his cross wanton wife. Part II. The sudden surprise; or, Will the weaver catch'd in the funnel of a chimney by the young cuckold. Part III. The young cuckold's great poilcy [sic]; or, the wanton wife made honest.'

Evans, Pitts and Catnach each printed the same seventeen-stanza version at the beginning of the nineteenth century. Their successors reduced this to seven double stanzas, and this was followed by provincial printers in Birmingham, Liverpool, Preston and Stirling. See Bodleian, Harding B 25(2078) (Evans; mostly illegible); Firth c.18(255) and Harding B 16(310b) (Pitts); Harding B 11(4247) and Firth c.18(254) (Such); and Harding B 28(151) and Harding B 28(179) (Armstrong of Liverpool). It was also printed in Boston, Massachusetts, c.1813–14.

Daniel Newman's text was a little confused in places, and has been edited to restore rhymes and scansion. It is also amended in places from broadside copies. His final line ought to be noted as an alternative, more consistent with other oral and print versions: 'Sent him home with two black eyes'. A recording from English tradition can be heard on Veteran VTC6CD, *It was on a Market Day 1* (Buster Mushtoe, Worcestershire), and an American example at the website of the Max Hunter Collection (Ollie Gilbert, Arkansas: 'Billy Beaver').

THE WONDERFUL SUCKING PIG

Roud 1615

Tune noted by Guyer. Ionian with inflexion of 7th.

One of the many 'wonder' songs popular in the early nineteenth century (see also 'The Crocodile'). Later examples of the genre, like this one, tended to mention earlier songs in the opening lines; here we have 'The Christmas Goose' (not in Roud, but see Bodleian, Harding B 16(49c) and Firth c.19(246), for two songs on the subject) and 'The Great Pie' (Roud 8092). Disley of London printed it as 'The Christmas Sucking Pig' around 1870, and T Taylor of London, between 1859 and 1899, as 'The Wonderful Sucking Pig'; for this last, see Bodleian, Harding B 11(4299).

Alfred Stride had forgotten some lines, so verses 5 and 6 here are made from his incomplete verses 5, 6 and 7. In verse 3, 'the comet' has been amended to the more general 'a comet'; it seems not unlikely, though, that 'the Comet', as it is printed in Taylor's edition, was Haley's, which had made one of its appearances in 1835. A 'quartern buster', incidentally, was a large loaf made from a quartern (four pounds) of flour. Buster (usually 'burster' until *c*.1850) was common slang for a loaf or large bun; but also for 'anything of superior size or astounding nature'. (Partridge, *Dictionary of Slang and Unconventional English*). The song has not been much found in tradition; Jack Elliott of Birtley used to sing it, and Bob Lewis of Sussex has a version which can be heard on Veteran VTC4CD, *Down in the Fields*.

YOUNG EMMA

Roud 182 Laws M34

Widely printed in England and Scotland. The earliest broadsides are from Pitts and Catnach, and the song is probably not older than the early nineteenth century. Pitts and Catnach both had nine double stanzas, but some later versions have acquired a further stanza (Mr Elliott's verses 5 and 6). See Bodleian, Harding B 11(1433) (Pitts: 'Young Edmund in the Lowlands Low'); Johnson Ballads 214 (Catnach: 'Young Edwin in the Lowlands Low'); and others under various forms of the latter title, plus Harding B 17(81b) 'Edwin in the Lowlands Low', which is quite close to our text.

Joseph Elliott's text is amended in places, mainly to restore rhymes and make the story easier to follow; a few original readings are worth pointing out. In verse 4 he sang either 'come round his head' or 'crowned his head'; the latter is the broadside form. In verse 6 he sang dialectal 'drave' or 'draved' instead of 'dragged', and in verse 13 'ramping' rather than 'ranting'.

Oral versions are common in Britain and Ireland, the USA and Canada. The Catnach print specified the tune 'Bushes and Briars', but the song has been found sung to a wide range of melodies. Some examples can be heard on Kyloe 101, *Travellers' Tales 2* (Gabrielle Ijdo, Aberdeenshire: 'Young Emslie'); Musical Traditions MTCD329–0, *The Hardy Sons of Dan* and Veteran VT134CD, *Linkin' o'er the Lea* (Maggie Murphy, Fermanagh: 'Young Edmund'); Topic TSCD667, *It Fell on a Day, a Bonny Summer Day* (Harry Cox, Norfolk: Young Edmund') and TSCD653, *O'er His Grave the Grass Grew Green* (Geordie Hanna, Tyrone: 'Young Edmund in the Lowlands Low').

THE YOUNG SAILOR CUT DOWN IN HIS PRIME

Roud 2 Laws Q26

The earliest surviving broadside is a six-stanza slip apparently of the late eighteenth century, 'The Buck's Elegy', set in Covent Garden (Madden Collection; Holloway & Black, I, 48–9). The song is likely older, perhaps mid C18; P W Joyce printed a single, slightly garbled, verse given to him in 1848 by a man who remembered it being sung in Cork 'about 1790'.

Such of London, Pratt of Birmingham and various northern printers of the mid-nineteenth century printed a six-stanza version, 'The Unfortunate Lad', which mentions 'Lock Hospital' (established in 1746 at Hyde Park Corner for the treatment of venereal diseases; the name became generic and many such 'Lock Hospitals' were subsequently opened). See Bodleian, Harding B 15(341a) and other editions without imprint. Only one broadside mentions the Royal Albion; 'The Sailor Cut Down in his Prime' printed by Forth of Hull. There were plenty of Royal Albion hotels, the most famous being the Brighton one founded in 1826, but it is frequently suggested that 'Royal Albert', which occurs in several oral versions, is the earlier form. The Royal Albert Dock opened in 1880 and Forth was still printing when William Curtis' version was collected, so this is certainly possible.

The song has been enormously popular in a variety of forms which usually retain the military funeral. It was re-cast as 'The Young Girl Cut Down in Her Prime' (*CEFS* 74) and is well known in America as 'The Streets of Laredo' and 'St James' Infirmary' among many other variations. The tunes used are mostly related to each other, though they vary considerably in detail and modal form.

Examples from tradition can be heard on Musical Traditions MTCD309–10, *Just Another Saturday Night* (Harry Holman, Sussex: 'Young Sailor Cut Down') and MTCD301–2, *A Broadside* (Bob Hart, Suffolk: 'Young Sailor Cut Down in His Prime'); Veteran VT153CD *Romany Roots* (Vic Legg, Cornwall: 'Young Sailor Cut Down'), VTD148CD, *A Shropshire Lad* (Fred Jordan, Shropshire: 'Royal Albert') and VT119CD *Catch Me if You Can* (Charlotte Legg, Cornwall: 'Sailor Cut Down in His Prime'); Topic TSCD662, *We've Received Orders to Sail* (Johnny Doughty, Sussex: 'Streets of Port Arthur') and TSCD652, *My Ship Shall Sail the Ocean* (Harry Upton, Sussex: 'Royal Albion').

See also Kenneth Lodewick, '"The Unfortunate Rake" and His Descendants' in *Western Folklore*, XIV (1955) 144–161, and David Atkinson, '"The Unfortunate Rake" – a Song Trail' in *Root and Branch I: A New World* (EFDSS, 1999) which also includes recordings of versions from Johnny Doughty, Almeda Riddle ('Tom Sherman's Barroom') and Doc Watson ('St James' Hospital').

In 1959, Frank Purslow and John Pearse recorded several songs from the Hammond, Gardiner and Sharp collections for Dobell's Folklore label; the LP was released in 1960 as *Rap A Tap Tap – English Folk Songs Miss Pringle Never Taught Us* (Folklore F–LEUT 1). It seems to have been re-released under several titles, including (in the USA) *Unexpurgated Songs of Erotica: Witty Ditties of Passion and Pleasure: A Naughty, Bawdy Songfest of English Erotica* (FAX Records FAXLP–1010, n.d.) The original sessions were recorded by Peter Kennedy at Cecil Sharp House, and were reissued by him, first on cassette (1987) and later on CDR, as *Bottoms Up: Folk Songs Miss Pringle Never Taught Us* (FolkTrax FTX–219).

In the 1970s, Forest Tracks released two LPs of performances by local singers of songs from Frank Purslow's books, *Folk Songs from Hampshire* (FT2006, 1974) and *Folk Songs from Dorset* (FT3007, 1975). These have now been re-released as a double CDR, *Folk Songs from Hampshire and Dorset* (FTBT 2CD1), with additional material. http://www.forest-tracks.co.uk/

BIBLIOGRAPHIES

THESE listings replace the bibliography included in the original edition. For a wider range of references, readers should consult David Atkinson's *English Folk Song: An Introductory Bibliography Based on the Holdings of the Vaughan Williams Memorial Library*, the third edition of which is available in pdf format at the EFDSS website: http://www.efdss.org/

Abbreviations

Books referred to in the Notes by abbreviated titles:

Broadwood: Lucy Broadwood and J A Fuller Maitland, eds, *English County Songs* (London: Leadenhall Press, 1893).

Bronson: Bertrand Harris Bronson, ed., *The Traditional Tunes of the Child Ballads, with their Texts, According to the Extant Records of Great Britain and America*, 4 vols (Princeton: Princeton University Press, 1959–72).

Chappell: William Chappell, ed., *Popular Music of the Olden Time: A Collection of Ancient Songs, Ballads, and Dance Tunes, Illustrative of the National Music of England*, 2 vols (London: Cramer, Beale and Chappell, 1855–59; repr New York: Dover, 1965).

CEFS: R Vaughan Williams and A L Lloyd, eds, *The Penguin Book of English Folk Songs: From the Journal of the Folk Song Society and the Journal of the English Folk Dance and Song Society* (Harmondsworth: Penguin, 1959), reissued as *Classic English Folk Songs*, rev. by Malcolm Douglas (London: English Folk Dance & Song Society, 2003).

Child: Francis James Child, ed., *The English and Scottish Popular Ballads*, 5 vols (Boston: Houghton, Mifflin, 1882–98; repr New York: Dover, 1965 and Northfield, Minnesota: Loomis House Press, 2001–).

Dixon-Bell: James Henry Dixon, ed., *Ancient Poems, Ballads, and Songs of the Peasantry of England, Taken Down from Oral Recitation, and Transcribed from Private Manuscripts, Rare Broadsides, and Scarce Publications* (London: T Richards for the Percy Society, 1846; rev. by Robert Bell, London: John W Parker, 1857).

Everlasting Circle: James Reeves, ed., *The Everlasting Circle: English Traditional Verse, Edited with an Introduction and Notes from the Manuscripts of S Baring-Gould, H E D Hammond and George B Gardiner* (London: Heinemann, 1960).

FMJ: *Folk Music Journal* (London: English Folk Dance and Song Society, 1965–).

FSJ: *Journal of the Folk-Song Society* (London, 1899–1931).

Garland: Sabine Baring-Gould and H Fleetwood Sheppard, eds, *A Garland of Country Song: English Folk Songs with their Traditional Melodies* (London: Methuen, 1895; repr Felinfach: Llanerch, 1998).

Greig-Duncan: Patrick Shuldham-Shaw, Emily B Lyle and others, eds, *The Greig-Duncan Folk Song Collection*, 8 vols (Aberdeen: Aberdeen University Press / Mercat Press, 1981–2002).

Harker: David Harker, ed., *Songs from the Manuscript Collection of John Bell* (Surtees Society, vol CXCVI, 1985).

Holloway and Black: John Holloway and Joan Black, eds, *Later English Broadside Ballads*, 2 vols (London: Routledge & Kegan Paul, 1975–79).

Idiom of the People: James Reeves ed., *The Idiom of the People: English Traditional Verse Edited with an Introduction and Notes from the Manuscripts of Cecil J. Sharp* (London: Heinemann, 1958).

JEFDSS: *Journal of the English Folk Dance and Song Society* (London, 1931–1964).

Joyce: Patrick Weston Joyce, ed., *Ancient Irish Music* (Dublin: McGlashan and Gill, 1873).

Karpeles: Maud Karpeles, *Cecil Sharp's Collection of English Folk Songs*, 2 vols (London: Oxford University Press, 1974).

Kidson: Frank Kidson, ed., *Traditional Tunes* (Oxford: Chas Taphouse, 1891; repr Felinfach: Llanerch, 1999).

Kinloch: George Ritchie Kinloch, ed., *The Ballad Book* (Edinburgh, 1827; repr in *Choice Old Scottish Ballads*, Wakefield: E P Publishing, 1976).

ODNR: Iona and Peter Opie, eds, *The Oxford Dictionary of Nursery Rhymes* (Oxford: Clarendon Press, 1951; 2nd impression with corrections, 1952).

Pedlar's Pack: W H Logan, ed., *A Pedlar's Pack of Ballads and Songs* (Edinburgh, 1869).

Petrie: Charles Villiers Stanford, ed., *The Complete Collection of Irish Music As Noted by George Petrie (1789–1866)*, 3 vols (London: Irish Literary Society, 1902–5; repr Felinfach: Llanerch, 1994).

Pills: Thomas D'Urfey, ed., *Wit and Mirth: Or Pills to Purge Melancholy*, 6 vols (London, 1719–20; rpr in 3 vols, New York: Folklore Library Publishers, 1959).

Pinto & Rodway: Vivian de Sola Pinto and Allan Edwin Rodway, eds, *The Common Muse: An Anthology of Popular British Ballad Poetry, XVth–XXth century* (London: Chatto & Windus, 1957; repr Penguin, 1965).

Renwick: Roger de V Renwick, *English Folk Poetry: Structure and Meaning* (London: Batsford, 1980).

Roxburghe: William Chappell and J Woodfall Ebsworth, eds, *The Roxburghe Ballads*, 9 vols (London and Hertford: Ballad Society, 1869–99).

Simpson: Claude M Simpson, ed., *The British Broadside Ballad and Its Music* (New Brunswick: Rutgers University Press, 1966).

SMM: James Johnson, ed., *The Scots Musical Museum*, 6 vols (Edinburgh: 1787–1803; repr in 2 vols, Portland, Oregon: Amadeus Press, 1991).

Williams: Alfred Williams, ed., *Folk-Songs of the Upper Thames, with an Essay on Folk-Song Activity in the Upper Thames Neighbourhood* (London: Duckworth, 1923).

The Hammond and Gardiner Collections

Songs from the MSS have appeared in a number of publications over the years. See in particular the following:

Brocklebank, Joan, and Biddie Kindersley, eds, *A Dorset Book of Folk Songs* (London: EFDSS, 1948). A small selection from the Hammond collection.

Browne, John Paddy, ed., *Folk Songs of Old Hampshire* (Horndean: Milestone Publications, 1987). Songs about Hampshire and folk songs collected in Hampshire, including some from Gardiner.

Copper, Bob, *Songs and Southern Breezes, Country Folk and Country Ways* (London, Heinemann, 1973). Includes songs from Hampshire and material relating to some of Gardiner's singers and their successors.

Gardiner, George B, *Folk Songs from Hampshire*, with pianoforte accompaniment by Gustav von Holst, *Folk-Songs of England*, Book III (London: Novello, 1909). 16 songs; repr. in Sharp, Cecil J, ed., *English County Folk Songs* (London: Novello, 1961). Some of the tunes have had different texts set to them.

Hammond, H E D, *Folk Songs from Dorset*, with pianoforte accompaniment by Cecil J Sharp, *Folk-Songs of England*, Book I (London: Novello, 1908). 16 songs; repr. in Sharp, Cecil J, ed., *English County Folk Songs* (London: Novello, 1961).

Journal of the Folk-Song Society (1899–1931):
II (7) 1905: several songs 'communicated by Dr Gardiner'.
III (10) 1907, 47–58: several songs from southern England, including material from Hammond and Gardiner.
III (11) 1907, 59–136: songs from the Hammond collection.
III (13) 1909, 247–317: songs from the Gardiner collection.
VII (27) 1923, 31–94: songs from the Hammond collection.
VIII (34) 1930, 177–217: songs from the Hammond collection.

Folk Music Journal (1965–):
I (3) 1967, 129–157: Frank Purslow, 'The George Gardiner Folk Song Collection (with ten songs)'.
I (4) 1968, 236–266: Frank Purslow, 'The Hammond Brothers' Folk Song Collection (with nine songs)'.

Palmer, Roy, ed., *Folk Songs Collected by Ralph Vaughan Williams* (London: Dent, 1983; repr. with corrections as *Bushes and Briars: Folk Songs Collected by Ralph Vaughan Williams*, Felinfach: Llanerch, 1999). Most of the Hampshire songs included were actually collected by Gardiner and Gamblin; RVW later re-notated them, either in person or from phonograph records, for the Folk-Song Society.

Purslow, Frank, ed:
Marrow Bones: English Folk Songs from the Hammond and Gardiner Mss. (London: E.F.D.S. Publications, 1965).
The Wanton Seed: More English Folk Songs from the Hammond & Gardiner Mss. (London: E.F.D.S. Publications, 1968).
The Constant Lovers: More English Folk Songs from the Hammond & Gardiner Mss. (London: E.F.D.S. Publications, 1972).
The Foggy Dew: More English Folk Songs from the Hammond & Gardiner Mss. (London: E.F.D.S. Publications, 1974).

Reeves, James, ed., *The Everlasting Circle: English Traditional Verse, Edited with an Introduction and Notes from the Manuscripts of S Baring-Gould, H E D Hammond and George B Gardiner* (London: Heinemann, 1960). Includes a large number of texts (without their tunes) from the Hammond and Gardiner collections.

Sedley, Stephen, ed., The Seeds of Love: A Comprehensive Anthology of Folk Songs of the British Isles (London: Essex Music, 1967). A selection of heavily collated songs which include material from the Hammond and Gardiner collections.

Vaughan Williams, R, and A L Lloyd, eds, *The Penguin Book of English Folk Songs: From the Journal of the Folk Song Society and the Journal of the English Folk Dance and Song Society* (Harmondsworth: Penguin, 1959). Reissued as *Classic English Folk Songs*, rev. by Malcolm Douglas (London: English Folk Dance & Song Society in association with the South Riding Folk Network, 2003). Includes several songs deriving in whole or in part from the Hammond and Gardiner MSS.

Specialist Record Labels

Elphinstone Institute (University of Aberdeen)
Books and recordings concentrating on the north east Scottish tradition.
http://www.abdn.ac.uk/elphinstone/

Folktrax
Field recordings made by the late Peter Kennedy and others from 1950 onwards. Includes a large amount of important material; copies available on CDR. http://www.folktrax.org/

Greentrax Records
Recordings of traditional and revival singers and musicians from Scotland. Includes the School of Scottish Studies' *Scottish Tradition* series. http://www.greentrax.com/

Helions Bumpstead Gramophone Company
Recordings made by Neil Langham of traditional song and music in Suffolk. http://www.traditionsofsuffolk.com/

Kyloe Records
Traditional music, song and storytelling from the north of England and Scotland. Includes recordings made by Mike Yates and Hamish Henderson. http://www.kyloerecords.co.uk/

Musical Traditions
CDRs of traditional singers and musicians with accompanying booklets containing substantial background and documentation. http://www.mustrad.org.uk/records.htm

Rounder Records
Catalogue includes material recorded by Alan Lomax in America and Europe. http://www.rounder.com/

Topic Records
Extensive catalogue of recordings of traditional and revival singers and musicians, including the epic *Voice of the People* series. http://www.topicrecords.co.uk/

Veteran
New and archive recordings of traditional singers and musicians from England and Ireland. http://www.veteran.co.uk/

Internet Resources: General

British Library: Traditional Music in England
Catalogues of collections of field recordings held by the National Sound Archive. http://www.bl.uk/collections/sound-archive/traditional_music.html

British Library: Collect Britain
Includes 59 wax cylinder recordings from the EFDSS collections. Most are of Scottish Gaelic song, but there is some English material. http://www.collectbritain.co.uk/collections/wax/

English Folk Dance and Song Society
Traditional music, song and dance resources; includes websites for *Folk Music Journal* (http://fmj.efdss.org/) and *English Dance and Song* magazine (http://eds.efdss.org/). A series of webpages devoted to additions, corrections and supplementary material for this book will shortly be available there. http://efdss.org/

Folkopedia
A 'Wiki' dedicated to the Folk Arts of England and beyond. Launched recently by EFDSS, it is a peer reviewed resource for students, teachers and enthusiasts. http://folkopedia.efdss.org/

John Quincy Wolf Collection
Ozark songs recorded between 1952 and 1963 with text and audio. Includes versions of some songs in this book. http://www.lyon.edu/wolfcollection/

Max Hunter Folk Song Collection
Extensive archive of Ozark Mountain songs recorded between 1956 and 1976 with text, audio and staff notation. Much of the material is of British origin, and a number of the songs in this book are included, sometimes in multiple versions. http://maxhunter.missouristate.edu/

Musical Traditions
Online magazine including a wide range of articles relevant to the subject of this book. http://www.mustrad.org.uk/

Roud Folk Song and Broadside Indexes
The most important finding aid in existence for students of folk song, compiled and constantly updated by Steve Roud. http://library.efdss.org/

Vaughan Williams Memorial Library
Includes searchable indexes of the Broadwood, Collinson, Gardiner, Grainger, Hammond, Karpeles, Sharp and Vaughan Williams song collections, the Roud Folk Song and Broadside Indexes and Bibliography, and photographs from the Sharp collection. http://library.efdss.org/

Broadsides and Cheap Print

Collison, Robert, *The Story of Street Literature: Forerunner of the Popular Press* (London: Dent, 1973).

Dugaw, Dianne M., 'Anglo-American Folksong Reconsidered: The Interface of Oral and Written Forms', *Western Folklore*, 43 (1984), 83–103.

Dugaw, Dianne, 'The Popular Marketing of "Old Ballads": The Ballad Revival and Eighteenth-Century Antiquarianism Reconsidered', *Eighteenth-Century Studies*, 21 (1987), 71–90.

Dugaw, Dianne, 'Chapbook Publishing and the "Lore" of "the Folks"', in *The Other Print Tradition: Essays on Chapbooks, Broadsides, and Related Ephemera*, ed. Cathy Lynn Preston and Michael J. Preston, New Perspectives in Folklore, Vol. 3, Garland Reference Library of the Humanities, Vol. 1470 (New York: Garland, 1995), pp. 3–18.

Gregory, Rosaleen and David, 'Jewels Left in the Dung-hills: Broadside and Other Vernacular Ballads Rejected by Francis Child', *Canadian Journal for Traditional Music / Revue de musique folklorique canadienne*, 29 (2002), 69–80.

Laws, G. Malcolm, Jr, *American Balladry from British Broadsides: A Guide for Students and Collectors of Traditional Song*, Publications of the American Folklore Society, Bibliographical and Special Series, Vol. 8 (Philadelphia: American Folklore Society, 1957).

Livingston, Carole Rose, *British Broadside Ballads of the Sixteenth Century: A Catalogue of the Extant Sheets and an Essay*, Garland Reference Library of the Humanities, Vol. 1390 (New York and London: Garland, 1991).

Neuburg, Victor E., *Popular Literature: A History and Guide from the Beginning of Printing to the Year 1897* (London: Woburn Press, 1977).

Palmer, Roy, '"Veritable Dunghills": Professor Child and the Broadside', *Folk Music Journal*, 7 (1996), 155–66.

Renwick, Roger de V., 'The Oral Quality of a Printed Tradition', *Acta Ethnographica Hungarica*, 47 (2002), 81–89; repr. in *Folk Ballads, Ethics, Moral Issues*, ed. by Gábor Barna and Ildikó Kríza, Papers of the 31st International Ballad Conference, Budapest 21–23 April 2001, Szegedi Vallási Néprajzi Könyvtár / Bibliotheca Religionis Popularis Szegediensis, 10 (Budapest: Akadémiai Kiadó, 2002), pp. 81–89.

Rollins, Hyder E., 'The Black-Letter Broadside Ballad', *PMLA*, 34 (n.s. 27) (1919), 258–339.

Rollins, Hyder E., *An Analytical Index to the Ballad-Entries (1557–1709) in the Registers of the Company of Stationers of London* (Chapel Hill: University of North Carolina Press, 1924).

Shepard, Leslie, *The Broadside Ballad: A Study in Origins and Meaning* (London: Herbert Jenkins, 1962).

Shepard, Leslie, *The History of Street Literature: The Story of Broadside Ballads, Chapbooks, Proclamations, News-Sheets, Election Bills, Tracts, Pamphlets, Cocks, Catchpennies, and Other Ephemera* (Newton Abbott: David & Charles, 1973).

Simpson, Claude M., *The British Broadside Ballad and Its Music* (New Brunswick: Rutgers University Press, 1966).

Spufford, Margaret, 'The Pedlar, the Historian and the Folklorist: Seventeenth Century Communications', *Folklore*, 105 (1994), 13–24.

Spufford, Margaret, *Small Books and Pleasant Histories: Popular Fiction and its Readership in Seventeenth-Century England* (London: Methuen, 1981; rpt Past and Present Publications, Cambridge: Cambridge University Press, 1985).

Spufford, Margaret, *The Great Reclothing of Rural England: Petty Chapmen and their Wares in the Seventeenth Century*, History Series, Vol. 33 (London: Hambledon Press, 1984).

Thomson, Robert S., 'The Development of the Broadside Ballad Trade and Its Influence upon the Transmission of English Folksongs', PhD thesis, University of Cambridge, 1974.

Watt, Tessa, *Cheap Print and Popular Piety 1550–1640*, Cambridge Studies in Early Modern British History (Cambridge: Cambridge University Press, 1991).

Wehse, 'British and American Humorous Broadside Ballads (Schwank Songs): A Genre Neglected in Folklore Research', ARV: *Scandinavian Yearbook of Folklore*, 38 (1982), 133–53.

Wehse, Rainer, 'Broadside Ballad and Folksong: Oral Tradition versus Literary Tradition', *Folklore Forum*, 8 (1975), 324–34 [2–12].

Wehse, Rainer, 'Criticism in Humorous Narrative Broadside Songs', in *Narrative Folksong: New Directions: Essays in Appreciation of W. Edson Richmond*, ed. by Carol L. Edwards and Kathleen E. B. Manley (Boulder, CO: Westview Press, 1985), pp. 266–83.

Wehse, Rainer, *Schwanklied und Flugblatt in Großbritannien*, Artes Populares, Studia Ethnographica et Folkloristica, Band 3 (Frankfurt am Main: Peter Lang, 1979).

Würzbach, Natascha, 'An Approach to a Context-Oriented Genre Theory in Application to the History of the Ballad: Traditional Ballad – Street Ballad – Literary Ballad', *Poetics*, 12 (1983), 35–70.

Würzbach, Natascha, *The Rise of the English Street Ballad, 1550–1650*, translated by Gayna Walls, European Studies in English Literature (Cambridge: Cambridge University Press, 1990).

Broadsides: Internet Resources

This is a small selection of some of the more useful resources available at the time of writing.

America Singing: Nineteenth-Century Song Sheets
http://lcweb2.loc.gov/ammem/
The Rare Book and Special Collections Division of the Library of Congress holds 4291 song sheets or broadsides. Much of the material is American, but the British and Irish broadside presses are also represented. The collection spans the period from the turn of the nineteenth century to the 1880s, the bulk being from the 1850s to the 1870s. The catalogue can be searched or browsed, and both images of the sheets and html transcriptions of the texts are available.

Bodleian Library Broadside Ballads
http://www.bodley.ox.ac.uk/ballads/
The Bodleian Library of the University of Oxford has unparalleled holdings of over 30,000 ballads in several major collections. The original printed materials range from the sixteenth to the twentieth century. The Broadside Ballads project makes the digitised copies of the sheets and ballads available to the research community. The entire catalogue can be browsed or searched by a number of criteria.

The Dicey and Marshall Catalogue
http://www.diceyandmarshall.bham.ac.uk/
A reproduction of the 1764 catalogue issued by the prolific publishers of cheap print, Cluer Dicey and Richard Marshall. The titles of the text items are linked to modern bibliographical records.

Eighteenth Century (1701–1790) Cheap Print: a Finding Aid
http://www.18ccheap-print.bham.ac.uk/
An alphabetical listing of broadsides and the locations of copies, compiled by Richard C Simmons of the University of Birmingham.

Glasgow Broadside Ballads
http://www.cc.gla.ac.uk/courses/scottish/ballads/
A selection of digital images of nineteenth century broadside ballads from the David Murray Collection (Glasgow University Library Special Collections), chosen mainly for local or generally Scottish connections, though English and Irish material is also included; with introductory essays and note for students.

The Lester S Levy Collection of Sheet Music
http://levysheetmusic.mse.jhu.edu/
The collection is part of Special Collections at the Milton S Eisenhower Library of Johns Hopkins University. It contains over 29,000 pieces of music and focuses on popular American music spanning the period 1780 to 1960. Catalogue descriptions are fully indexed and searchable, and images of covers and music are also available for material published before 1923 and in the public domain. Although the focus is American, there is a lot of British material included. Particularly useful where parlour and stage songs have found their way into oral currency.

The Pepys Ballads
http://emc.english.ucsb.edu/ballad_project/
Early Modern Center, English Department, University of California at Santa Barbara. An online archive of the 1,857 ballads in the Samuel Pepys collection held at the Pepys Library, Magdalene College, Cambridge. Working from microfilm photographs of the originals, optimised images of each ballad have been prepared in several sizes, together with transcriptions into modern type which retain the text layout and woodcuts. There are also background essays and other supporting material, including modern mp3 recordings of some of the songs. The archive is catalogued using a system based on Helen Weinstein's indexes of the collection, and is searchable by various criteria.

Roots of Folk: Old English, Scots and Irish Songs and Tunes
http://www.csufresno.edu/folklore/Olson/
Compiled by the late Bruce Olson. A densely organised and scholarly series of indexes of early broadside ballads, ballad operas and their tunes. Includes tunes in abc format for sixteenth and seventeenth century broadsides (largely drawn from Claude M Simpson's book *The British Broadside Ballad and Its Music*), systems for tune comparison, song texts and examinations of the early history of various pieces.

The Roud Broadside Index
http://library.efdss.org/
Steve Roud's index of broadside ballads; a companion to the even more extensive Roud Folk Song Index. The indexes are searchable individually or together.

Streetprint: Revolution and Romanticism
http://www.crcstudio.arts.ualberta.ca/streetprint/
A private collection of street literature held in Edmonton, Alberta, Canada. It comprises a wide range of types, from street ballads through chapbooks and tracts to valentines, mostly from late eighteenth and early nineteenth century Britain. Digital images of the items are available, together with text transcriptions. The index can be searched or browsed by category.

The Word on the Street
http://www.nls.uk/broadsides/
The National Library of Scotland's online collection of nearly 1,800 broadsides, including many songsheets. Searchable by keyword or phrase, and browseable by title or subject. Images of the broadsides are available in jpg and pdf formats, with commentary and text transcriptions, supporting material, illustration and an introductory bibliography.

INDEX OF FIRST LINES